WILDLIFE
in Britain and Ireland

Books by the same author

At the Turn of the Tide
A Naturalist on Lindisfarne
Watching Sea Birds
In the High Grampians
The Watcher and the Red Deer
Life in Forest and Jungle

WILDLIFE
in Britain and Ireland

Richard
Perry

CROOM HELM LONDON

Croom Helm Ltd, 2-10 St John's Road, London SW11

British Library Cataloguing in Publication Data

Perry, Richard
Wildlife in Britain and Ireland.
1. Zoology – Great Britian
I. Title
591.9'41 QL255

ISBN 0-85664-306-8

FOR SAM AND ALEX FIFTEEN YEARS HENCE

Printed in Great Britain by
REDWOOD BURN LIMITED
Trowbridge & Esher

Contents

List of Illustrations

The World Wildlife Fund is happy to be associated with this fascinating account of the past riches and variety of Britain's wildlife, and the pressures our animals and plants have sadly, in many cases, failed to sustain down the ages.

'Wildlife in Britain and Ireland' is full of quotations and references which poignantly highlight the disappearance of our marshes and woods and the birds, mammals and insects which once filled them. The author Richard Perry closes on an optimistic note however, by reminding the reader of the comebacks that can be made by man-polluted habitats, and individual species, given the chance.

The World Wildlife Fund is an international fund-raising organisation whose work is devoted to ensuring the survival of animals and plants which are in danger of disappearing in Britain and many other parts of the world. Since 1961, the Fund has given over £15 million to nearly 1,900 projects in 100 countries.

For further information about the work of the World Wildlife Fund, please write to Panda House, 29 Greville Street, London EC1N 8AX.

It is the responsibility of all who are alive today
to accept the trusteeship of wildlife
and to hand on to posterity,
as a source of wonder and interest,
knowledge and enjoyment,
the entire wealth of diverse animals and plants.

This generation has no right
by selfishness
wanton or unintentional destruction,
or neglect,
to rob future generations of this great heritage.

Extermination of other creatures
is a disgrace to mankind.

The World Wildlife Charter 1962

Acknowledgements

Grateful acknowledgements to all those naturalists from whose works I have drawn freely, and to Prof. A.G. Tansley and his publishers, George Allen & Unwin, for permission to quote from *Britain's Green Mantle*, and to Anthony Dent and Harrap for permission to quote from *Lost Beasts of Britain*. Also to the reference department of the Northumberland County Central Library for once again obtaining large numbers of books and papers for me.

1978

Richard Perry
Northumberland

Introduction

Animals become extinct or decrease in numbers mainly because of the destruction of their habitat, or because they are unable to adapt to changes in this; but so long as the habitat is preserved they can survive considerable abuse. In the long term this destruction or alteration has been due to climatic vicissitudes, in the short term to man's activities – felling forests, draining marshes and gradually encroaching on the wilderness with his agricultural, industrial and urban development. He has also hunted and collected all forms of wildlife for several thousand years, and has finally polluted both the environment and its inhabitants with toxic chemicals. Today, the greater part of the British landscape, and of western Europe south of the wilder regions of Scandinavia, is man-made or has been considerably modified by him. There may be a few remote valleys or coastal tracts in Britain where nature is still virgin, but moors and hills have been grazed and burned for centuries, and the pristine ecology of the highest mountains in the Scottish Highlands is now endangered by the proliferation of Land Rover stalking roads, bulldozed to heights of over 3,000 feet, and by the ever-increasing erosion and fouling of the hills by skiers, climbers and hikers. But there is a happier obverse to this habitat destruction, in as much as conservation is becoming both acceptable and fashionable – always providing that it does not conflict with what is deemed to be the national interest – while twentieth-century man's green belts, parks and little woodlands probably harbour a greater variety and concentration of wildlife, particularly birds, than did the vast primeval forests. Thus, although this book is primarily a history of some aspects of wildlife ecology in Britain and, where relevant, western Europe, and of the relationships down the ages between different kinds of animals, it was impossible to consider these aspects without constant reference to man's own history and his almost universal impact on wildlife.

1 In the Beginning

During the Pleistocene series of ice ages which, including inter-glacial interludes, lasted for possibly 600,000 years, two-thirds of Britain was overlaid by an ice-sheet several hundred feet thick. Indeed, when the glaciation was at its most intense, the ice may have reached a depth of 3,500 or 4,000 feet over parts of the western Highlands of Scotland. But the ice-sheet never advanced south of a line extending approximately from the Thames to the Bristol Channel; even Dartmoor was apparently unglaciated.

Scandinavia, with the possible exception of a coastal strip of Norway, was also ice-capped, as were the Baltic and much of north-western Russia. To the south of the ice-sheet, however, tundra covered most of France and Germany and spread eastwards over Russia, where it merged with a zone of coniferous forest resembling the *taiga* of present-day Siberia. Deciduous woodlands in western Europe were therefore probably restricted to Iberia and the Mediterranean coastal regions.

During warmer inter-glacial periods of the Pleistocene Britain was intermittently inhabited by the Neanderthalers from perhaps 275,000 BP (Before the Present) until 70,000 or 35,000 BP, when their kind became extinct. They appear to have suffered from severe dietary deficiencies and also from bone diseases resulting from a lack of vitamin D, reputedly because, being black immigrants from the tropical zone, their pigmented skins could not absorb sufficient ultra-violet rays from the weaker northern sunlight. However that may be, it has been conjectured that some 'modern' mammals may have begun a continuous occupation of the more southerly ice-free areas of Britain during or even before the time of the Neanderthalers, though since conditions in southern Britain during the glacial periods must have been as severe as those prevailing today on the arctic tundras, it seems probable that this would have only been possible for such tundra and arctic species as reindeer, stoats, mountain hares or lemmings.

It would have been more feasible for a mammalian occupation – and also that of such butterflies as the large heath and the mountain ringlet

– to have begun during the third inter-glacial phase. The time scale prior to 10,000 BP is not exact, though it becomes more so after 4500 BP; but this particular phase is estimated to have lasted from around 185,000 to 115,000 BP, and to have enjoyed a temperate climate, warmer at times than that of today, with hot dry summers. Its scattered wooded 'parklands', which burgeoned into widespread forest during the warmer intervals, could have harboured red deer and roebuck, wolves, foxes, lynxes, martens, wild cats, badgers, beavers, otters and water voles; and their kind could have survived through the fourth and final ice age, and have been augmented by brown bears, wild boars, polecats, squirrels, shrews, bank voles and long-tailed field mice, since this glaciation was not as severe as the previous one, and the ice-sheet did not extend further south than north Norfolk, Wales and southern Ireland. It was, however, of long duration, for the ice did not begin to recede from lowland areas until 25,000 or 20,000 BP and did not finally vanish from northern Scotland until about 8000 BP. Thus the fluctuations in the advance and recession of the ice-sheet, and the complementary to and fro migrations of the Pleistocene fauna, are to be measured in tens of thousands of years. As G. B. Corbet has written in *The Terrestrial Mammals of Western Europe*:

> If we had been living at the northern boundary of the coniferous zone . . . we would only have been aware that any advance of the glaciation was in progress because young trees were looking weak and stunted in areas where the remnants of old trees showed them to have grown rather more strongly in their youth.

No doubt men were making their first slight impact on the wildlife of Britain by hunting at least as early as the late Old Stone Age when, as Graham Clark has surmised in *Prehistoric England*, their appetite for meat was sharpened by the rigours of a late glacial climate, though he suggests that the total human population in Britain at any one time in those early years may never have exceeded three or four hundred. Certainly in Europe the caves and shelters of Neanderthal men contain the bones of reindeer, bison and woolly mammoths, together with large quantities of willow-grouse and ptarmigan – tundra birds; while the superbly realistic cave paintings in south-west France and northern Spain bear witness to the fact that the Cromagnons, who inhabited Europe from about 35,000 to 15,000 BP, were hunting mammoths, bison and the great wild oxen (the urus or aurochs), in addition to elk, red deer, reindeer, boar and the small wild horses. These they killed with bow and arrow, spears tipped with ivory or bone, flint-bladed harpoons and throwing-sticks, and also by means of traps, ambuscades, stampedes and fire. Such typical tundra birds as snowy owls and ravens – the latter equally at home in frozen arctic wastes and burning deserts – were also depicted by them.

However the Cromagnons, being primarily hunters in order to obtain food, may have realised the necessity of preserving the stocks of game, and have been the first conservationists in western Europe. H. Breuil has stressed in *The Art of the Stone Age* that the Cromagnons were subjected to strong visual and dynamic impressions from the dangers to which they were exposed while hunting. In surviving these they acquired a unique knowledge of the habits, actions and anatomy of their various quarry, which the artists among them were inspired to reproduce in rock paintings and line drawings engraved on the walls of caves. These also expressed the social and religious structure of the hunter's culture:

> It was a matter of concern that the stock of animals, decimated by hunting and natural causes, should continually be replenished. As in all hunter cultures, recourse was had to magic, to the performance of death and fertility rites . . . by confining the animal within the limits of a painting one subjected it to one's power in the hunting grounds.

We know that a few Cromagnons ventured as far north as Britain – perhaps as many as two thousand during the summers, of whom a tenth might over-winter; but they left no cave paintings because, as we have seen, in contrast to the warmer regions of southern Europe, Britain was still a sub-arctic tundra in which the only practicable life was the nomadic one of following the herds of reindeer and horses. There was no leisure for cave art.

If it was not in fact practicable for any of Britain's mammals to have become permanently established during the Pleistocene, they must certainly have been able to by 14,000 or 11,000 BP, for during the pre-Boreal or sub-arctic phase, which began about that time, there was a comparatively rapid change in these islands to a Continental-type climate of contrasting seasons, with temperatures rising from arctic or sub-arctic levels to eight or nine degrees higher in the summer than those of today, as the ice-sheet finally receded from lowland areas and most of the country was opened to immigration and colonisation. The ice was replaced by great lakes and swamps (pathetically reflected in our present wet-lands), and the arctic-alpine flora of the tundra south of the ice gave way to juniper, dwarf willow and birch scrub, and ultimately to pine, which eventually dominated the forests. The tundra fauna was replaced by a forest one of red deer, elk, aurochs and boar, together with such predators as wolves, lynxes and bears.

At that time Britain was still joined to that part of Europe we know as Jutland and the Netherlands, with the sea lying north of the Dogger Bank, and the Thames a tributary of the Rhine, which flowed northwards through a plain of fens and open birchwoods. Small groups of Mesolithic tribesmen, whose hunting armoury had been supplemented by flake axes and the bolas, traversed the plain, hunting aurochsen, boar, elk, roe deer and especially red deer, whose antlers were used in

1. *Le Cheval Chinois*/Cave Painting of a Horse at Lascaux, France

see over

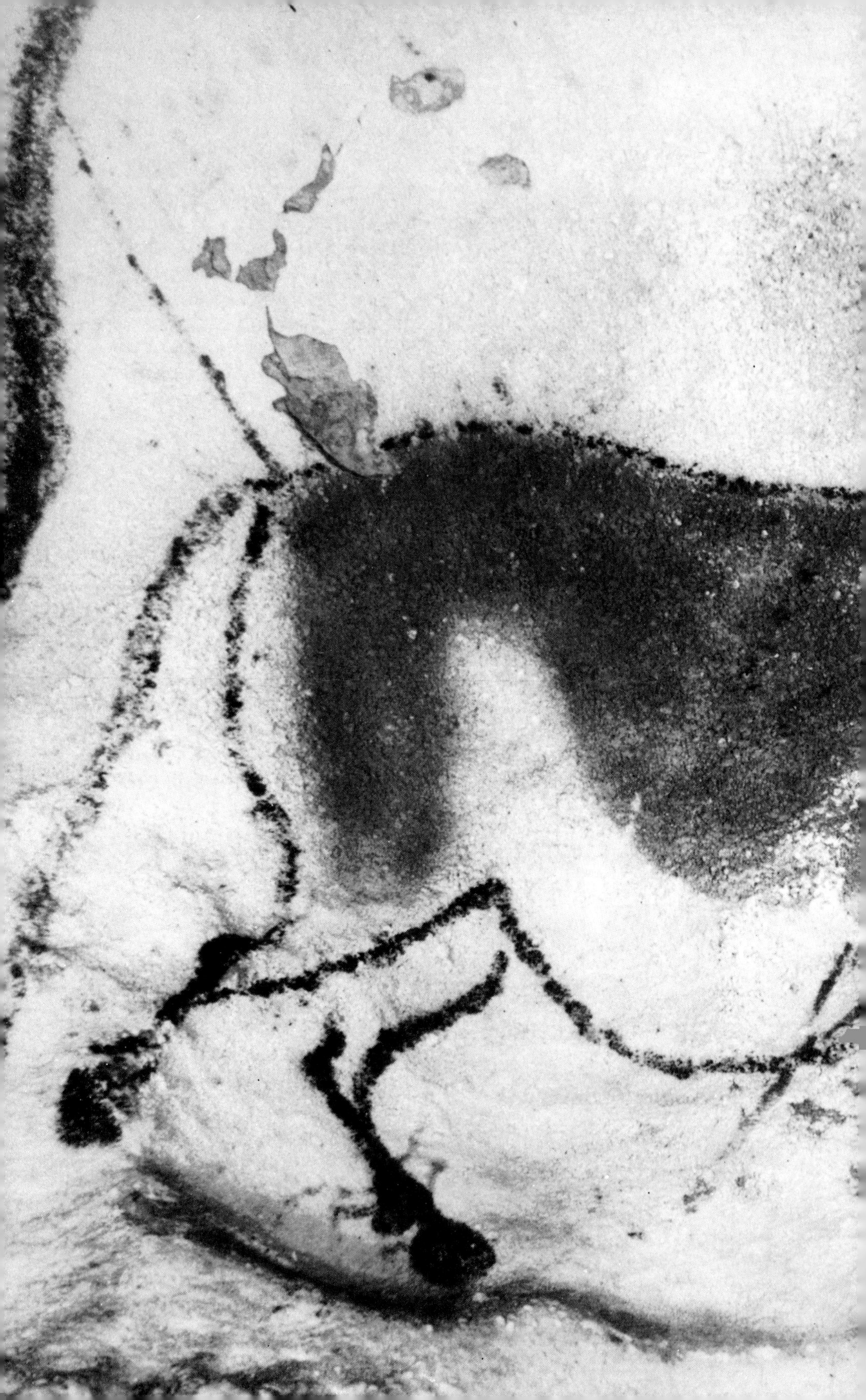

hunting ceremonies and also as frontlets when stalking up to their quarry. They were fishermen too, for carvings and engravings of the Magdalenian culture, which succeeded that of the Cromagnons, depicted pike and eels and especially trout and salmon (an antler baton from a French cave is engraved with four salmon and a pair of reindeer), while a forest culture known as the Maglemosian, identified in Kent, East Anglia, the West Riding of Yorkshire and south-east Scotland, and also in Scandinavia and north-west Russia, included the use of fish-hooks, nets, harpoons and dug-out canoes propelled by broad-bladed wooden paddles. The settlement at Star Carr near Scarborough, dated between 9100 and 9800 BP, produced large numbers of wooden-hafted fish spears, the heads of which had been fashioned from slivers of red deer antlers and pointed and serrated into barbs by whittling with flint knives and scrapers. Much the most numerous animal remains at this settlement were those of red deer, but roebuck, elk, boar, aurochs, fox, pine marten, badger, beaver, hare and hedgehog were also present, together with crane, merganser, a pintail-type duck, red-throated diver, great crested grebe, dabchick and lapwing.

Seals and wildfowl were also hunted by the Mesolithic peoples, while shellfish must have formed an important food item, for the late Mesolithic or early Neolithic kitchen-middens in Denmark are composed of mounds of marine shells fifty feet wide and ten or twenty feet high and almost a quarter of a mile long. These must have accumulated over a period of centuries. At a later date the Bronze Age village of Skara Brae in Orkney was indeed buried to the tops of the hut walls in its midden, with the result that the village must finally have been almost underground. Further evidence that the Mesolithic folk were not solely and continuously nomadic hunters is suggested by pollen analysis from a Breckland clearing two hundred yards long and fifty yards wide near the edge of Hockham Mere – the site of a long-vanished lake seven miles north-east of Thetford. This analysis indicates a decrease in tree pollen about 6500 BP followed by the appearance of grass, ling and heather, and implies that some tribes were already creating forest clearings, and incidentally assisting in the dispersal of weeds for such birds as greenfinches, linnets and goldfinches, which are known to have been present in Britain from late glacial times.

The Mesolithic peoples may also have partially domesticated a number of wild animals including, it has been suggested, red deer. Although the Cromagnons are reputed to have tamed wolves to work for them as hunting-dogs, the oldest known domestic dogs in western Europe are associated with the Maglemose culture in Denmark, for an earlier 'dog' at Starr Carr was subsequently considered to be a young wolf. With the rapid warming up of southern Europe at this time and a correspondingly rapid increase in the human population, hunting must have become both more intensive and extensive. At the same time, the climatic change resulted in the extinction of some food animals and the migration of the tundra-grazing herds of game and horses from the new forests to the grassy plains in the north and east. Thus the hunters may have been obliged to look for new sources of food, one of which could have been provided by the domestication of wild animals, of which none were easier to rear from an early age than the young of deer and goats whose dams had been killed during hunts. As Russell Kyle has pointed out in an article in *Animals*, the beginning of domestication, and also of forest clearance, marked the point when man ceased to be at the mercy of his environment but sought to exert ever more active control over it and its wild fauna.

In Britain pre-Boreal climatic conditions prevailed into the Boreal phase from 9500 to 7500 BP, though the summers were slightly cooler, with mean July temperatures three or four degrees above those of today. In the earlier stages of this phase most of Britain was covered with pine forest, which must have resembled the remnant 'black woods' of Scotch fir or Scots pine in the Highlands, where each tree had ample growing room in which to expand both vertically and laterally. Dividing perhaps only three feet or six feet above the base, twenty feet in circumference, the gnarled trunk of the older giant pine, forking and re-forking, twisting and thrusting up candelabras of huge limbs, simulated some massive holly tree. However, in North Britain, pine forest was not then as widespread as birch wood, for again, pollen analysis suggests that the pines did not reach the central Highlands until about 7000 BP, some 1,500 years after their colonisation of southern England.

2 The Forest Sanctuary Utterly Destroyed

Throughout the Boreal phase the continuous melting of the northern glaciers was to prove a decisive factor in determining the final composition of Britain's mammalian fauna, for the North Sea reflooded, with the result that before the end of the phase a channel had been breached by a combination of erosion and subsidence through the land link with Europe, and Britain had become an island, as Ireland had become one at least 10,000 years earlier. Thereafter, no mammals or reptiles or amphibians – or, to be more exact, no wingless terrestrial vertebrates – would enter Britain except by human agency.

A few species of bats, such as the greater and lesser horseshoe, may have done so, but our knowledge of the early history of bats in Britain, and indeed of their present distribution and habits, is too sparse for any detailed account. Their original retreats must have been trees and caves. Ten of our fourteen species still use caves as winter roosts, if cellars, ice houses, grottos, mines and tunnels be included in this category, though during the summer months all inhabit trees or buildings. Thus, colonies of more than a thousand bats – notably pipistrelles – consisting of all the pregnant females of one species in the surrounding district, may congregate in a single building during the summer months from June to August, to nurse their young for the twenty-five days until they can fly. The use of buildings is no doubt a fairly recent adaptation, perhaps by preference, perhaps because of the widespread destruction of old deciduous trees in hedgerows and parklands; but it has proved disastrous, for there has been a widespread decline in the numbers of bats throughout Europe. This has probably been caused entirely by man. To his age-old superstitious dislike of them have now been added the more lethal dangers of pesticides and the loss of roosting sites in tunnels and caves. Large numbers of these have been filled with refuse, and opencast mining and motorway construction have destroyed most of the suitable mine systems excavated between 1750 and 1914. Moreover, extensive disturbance of hibernating colonies by speleologists and over-enthusiastic banders has rendered roosting sites in caves uninhabitable, and there

2. Pipistrelle Bats

is also a commercial trade in bats for museums, schools and research bodies. The result has been that at least two British species, the mouse-eared and the greater horseshoe – both cave-dwellers – are in danger of extinction. The latter indeed has apparently become extinct in Kent and the Isle of Wight since the end of the nineteenth century; its distribution in its south-west England headquarters has contracted; and the total population of greater horseshoes in Britain may have decreased during the past twenty years from about 2,500 to a fifth of that number.

If no mammals could enter Britain after the link with Europe had been breached then, conversely, there could be no withdrawal for those already established here. One result of this separation from Europe so relatively soon after the recession of the ice was that Britain's fauna, and particularly that of Ireland, was restricted to fewer species than that of the adjacent Continent. There are, for example, five species of shrews and five of voles in northern France, but only three shrews and three voles in England, and only one shrew in Ireland and no voles – until the recent startling discovery of bank voles in a limited area of the south-west. When and how did these reach Ireland? There are no weasels in Ireland, but stoats have been there long enough for the females to develop ten or twelve teats instead of the normal eight. Were breeding conditions particularly favourable in Ireland? There are no yellow-necked field mice, harvest mice or dormice, though in the *Brut y Tywysogion* by Layamon, an English priest who lived at Ernley (Arley Regis) on the upper Severn in the early thirteenth century, we read that in the summer of AD 893:

> Vermin of a strange species were seen in Ireland, similar to moles, with two long front teeth each; and they ate all the corn, all the pasture, and roots of grasses, and the hay ground, causing a famine in the country, and it is supposed the Pagans [Danes] took them there, and wished likewise to introduce them into the isle of Britain; but by prayers to God, alms to the poor, and righteous life, God sent a sharp frost during the summer weather, which destroyed these insects.

Moles, which at the end of the last glacial period survived only in Spain, but moved northwards as the ice receded, were able to colonise England before the Channel was breached, but not Ireland before the latter had been isolated. That moles have never established themselves further north in Europe than the southern fringes of Scandinavia can no doubt be attributed to the fact that their subterranean mode of life is only practicable in regions where frost is not too prolonged and does not penetrate the soil too deeply, for, with this exception, they have succeeded in colonising a wider range of habitats, from Britain across Eurasia to the Pacific coast, than almost any other mammal. In Britain these include, in addition to pasture and arable land, deciduous and even coniferous woodland, and moors and hills to a height of almost 3,000 feet, such apparently unsuitable environments as the peaty soil of the Fens and the sandy soil of Breckland. Only in the hedgeless 'prairies' of East Anglia are they absent, except at their edges.

Land subsidence continued throughout the Atlantic phase, which followed the Channel breach, and the Fenlands and Somerset levels were flooded by the sea. During this much wetter and more equable era from 7500 to 5000 BP, when temperatures dropped to present-day means, there was a decrease in the area of pine forest, except in Scotland, and a great increase in alder. The latter, together with elm, lime and above all oak forest, which included extensive tracts of hazel scrub, bramble and especially thorn, dominated the lowland regions of Britain. For five thousand years the oak was to form the typical English wood, until almost totally destroyed to meet the demands of shipbuilding, iron-smelting and agriculture from the sixteenth to the nineteenth centuries. There were oak forests too on the valley slopes of the hills and mountains in the west and north, including the straths of the central Highlands, though they were replaced on poorer and sandier soils and at higher levels by pine and straggling woods of silver and hairy birches that climbed to heights of at least 3,000 feet.

Graham Clark has suggested that the Mesolithic population of Britain at this time may still only have totalled three or four thousand, and that it would have been a rare event for more than fifteen persons to gather together except at tribal gatherings. But near the end of the Atlantic phase an increase in the area of beech woods and also, once again, of pine forest, preceded the arrival in Britain of Neolithic man, who was to make more of an impact, though still a comparatively slight one, on the faunal environment; for these New Stone Age people were the first farmers in Britain, growing wheat at least as early as 4000 BP and, towards the end of their era of little more than a thousand years, herding their turbary or peat sheep. The goat-like Soay sheep of St Kilda – fawn in colour or brown with buff-white underparts and rump, and standing only twenty-two inches at the shoulder – may be their nearest surviving relatives. No doubt these early farmers practised the typical shifting cultivation of primitive agriculturists: felling, burning and sowing their crops in the ashes, rich in potash, in temporary clearings, before moving on to fresh ground. This would have involved the repeated clearing of existing vegetation, mainly forest; and the blanket-bogs of Wales are known to have been formed by their activities and those of their domestic stock in the upland woods. These resulted in the opening up of the forest canopy, which, combined with the deterioration in climate, led to soil leaching and the formation of bog. However, the Neolithic peoples settled mainly on the light, easily cultivated soils of the windswept ridges and summits of the southern downlands, which were easily accessible by river and from which they could look out over the endless forest with its wild beasts and unknown spirits. Although the downs were by then well wooded with beech, and also ash, hawthorn, sloe, box, juniper and yew, these were more easily felled and burned than the waterlogged swamps of oak. For flints for their axes they hacked down through the chalk with red deer antlers, the beams of which were cut short and all except the brow-tine removed. They quarried very extensively, for, as Jacquetta Hawkes has described in *Prehistoric Britain*, in order to reach the big nodules of readily workable flint that lay bedded in the chalk,

> pits were sunk to a depth of as much as 50 feet, often with underground galleries to follow up and exploit the richest seams . . . Once a good seam had been struck, shaft after shaft was sunk until several hundred might be found in a single group, often with their galleries linked together to form a vast, intricate network far below ground.

When the climate became drier again, after the mild and moist Atlantic phase, the long warm summers that prevailed through the thirteen hundred years or so of the Bronze Age would have cut back tree growth on the dry downs, and the grazing sheep would have encroached further and further upon previously forested areas – though in these drier conditions pine forest spread over the eastern fenlands, and some of the moorland bogs dried out. Moreover, towards the end of the New Stone Age the Megalithic people, who engineered Stonehenge and Avebury, were clearing sufficient land to pasture cattle. No doubt they were aided in this by their swine trampling and rooting up the seedlings in the forest, and especially by their goats cleaning up the scrub, for goats would eat virtually anything of a shrubby or woody nature, taking advantage of deep snow to bark such trees as ash, elm, holly, rowan, hazel, willow and yew, and climbing into them to obtain leaves and twigs. They have indeed denuded much of southern Europe of all vegetation, including bramble, briar, ivy, gorse and heather, in addition to thistles, docks, nettles and other intractable weeds.

It is possible that goats were indigenous in Britain, and they have certainly inhabited the hills of Wales and the Western Highlands for a very long time; but it is generally considered more likely that they were introduced as domestic stock by Neolithic tribes about 4000 BP. In Wales they may have been taken up into the hills some two thousand years ago by Iron Age herdsmen to eat down the vegetation on dangerous crag ledges and thus discourage cattle from straying on to these when grazing on the hill; and many must have been left to run wild at these summer hafodydd or shielings when the cattle were gathered in the autumn. This practice continued until sheep gradually replaced cattle during the eighteenth century, and there were still very large numbers of goats up to the time that the hills began to be replanted with trees in the late eighteenth and early nineteenth centuries – for there had been extensive deforestation of the Welsh hills since the eleventh century. According to the eighteenth-century antiquarian and naturalist, Thomas Pennant, the Welsh farmers hunted the goats in the

3. Feral Goats

autumn in order to obtain tallow for candles and 'the haunches . . . are frequently salted and dried, and supply all the uses of bacon: this by the natives is called *Coch y wden* or hung venison.'

But goats were not compatible with plantations of trees, and today the total population of 'wild' goats in Wales has been reduced to about three hundred. Elsewhere, there are still feral herds in perhaps as many as eighty localities in Scotland, thirty-five localities in England and less than thirty in Ireland. The majority of these can be traced to stock that have escaped or have been turned out of domestic herds, for the billies are inveterate wanderers during the rutting season, travelling alone or in threes or fours up to fifty miles from their home range in search of the widely scattered bands of nannies; and domestic stock revert to the wild state in both habits and appearance very quickly, acquiring the characteristic long shaggy coat within as short a period as ten years of going feral. That only the hardiest strains shall survive is ensured by the kids being born during the severest winter weather from late January to late March.

The logistics of transporting and erecting the Wiltshire megaliths must have involved a considerable settled population, and the numbers of the late Neolithic inhabitants of Britain can hardly have been less than 20,000 and may have been nearer to 100,000. They would certainly have continued reclaiming grazing land from the forest, for, unlike their predecessors, they do not appear to have settled on the chalk downs, possibly because a lack of water in the high places, due to the increasingly dry climate, had rendered them uninhabitable, though throughout the lowlands waterlogged areas were pocked with countless shallow meres surrounded by marsh or fen with clumps of willows or alders. The Iron Age people indeed deliberately sited the Glastonbury lake-village – which was sacked shortly before the Roman Conquest – on three to four acres of meadowland liable to be flooded during the winter and spring, but well adapted to defence, since it was probably surrounded by marshes. There, after clearing the alders and willows, they constructed an artificial island on the peat of closely packed, horizontal logs up to four feet thick, cemented together with clay, stones, brushwood and bracken, and enclosed by a palisade. At its maximum extent of some 10,500 square yards this island supported eighty or ninety round wattle huts thatched with reeds. But despite the curious siting of their village the Glastonbury folk kept horses of about twelve hands – which they both rode and drove, bridling them with bits fashioned from antlers – small Celtic cattle, pigs, sheep and a few goats, dogs and poultry, and cultivated wheat, barley and peas. They appear to have been agriculturalists rather than hunters, for though they left numerous tools, including extraordinary numbers of long-handled weaving combs, fashioned from the antlers of red and roe deer, most of the antlers appear to have been shed naturally; and though the bone remains in the village featured those of several beavers, there were very few of boars, foxes, martens, wild cats, stoats or hedgehogs. However, other mammals represented in this invaluable Iron Age inventory were polecats, water voles, bank voles, field voles and field mice, while the wildfowl that the villagers shot with unbaked clay sling-pellets included numerous cranes, whooper swans, cormorants, coots and mallard, but very few geese. Other apparently identifiable birds were bitterns, adult and young pelicans, teal, tufted duck, scaup, pochard and merganser, dabchicks, corncrakes, sea eagles, goshawks, kites, barn owls and carrion crows.

The Glastonbury villagers also fished for roach, perch, trout and shad, taking these almost exclusively with lead net-sinkers, though also spearing larger fish such as salmon and pike. So widespread has been man's interference with the fresh-water fishes of Britain that it would be unprofitable to attempt any general survey of their history, for the various species have been continuously redistributed by anglers and augmented by the introduction of exotics and game fish. An exception, however, is that most northerly fresh-water fish in Europe, the char, which, unlike its relatives the salmon and sea trout, has been impounded since the last glacial era in deep, cold lakes and lochs in Wales, the Lake District and the Highlands and Islands, and has been denied access to or from the sea, though some of the dozen or more endemic races that have evolved in isolation still migrate from their lakes to spawn during the winter in tributary streams. Now unable to exist in waters warmer than 60°F, they swim near the bottom during the daytime, when some races feed on molluscs, surfacing in large shoals at night to take the rising zoo-plankton.

By the beginning of the sub-Atlantic phase about 2550 BP the climate had become much wetter and cooler and, with its windy periods, resembled that of the present day; there were indeed to be no further notable climatic changes. Many tracts of pine and birch forest were overwhelmed by vast swamps and marshes, while deposits of peat, reforming the bogs and fens, preserved the brushwood tracks or 'corduroy' roads laid across them by the early Iron Age immigrants, whom the change in climate throughout Europe, coupled with a general land shortage, had driven into Britain. This was a time of intensive human migration, for northern peoples, whose harvests were dependent on dry warm summers, could no longer support life when these became wet and cool, and Western Europe was overrun again and again by peoples from the north and east threatened by famine. It seems unlikely that such widespread movements could have taken place without the deliberate or accidental introduction of various forms of animal life, both domesticated and wild, to new habitats, though there is no factual evidence of any such introductions to Britain. But it was not until about 100 or 75 BC that man began to make the first major impact on the natural environment in Britain, and to mark the beginning of the end for some of the forest fauna after a residence of at least ten thousand years; for it was at that time that the Belgae, a Celtic tribe of the late Iron Age, reached Britain shortly before the first Roman invasion. With their iron axes and heavy four-ox wheeled ploughs, the Belgae were sufficiently advanced agriculturalists to be able to cultivate wooded ground and export both corn and cattle to Europe. Their agricultural expansion entailed much destruction of forest, and south-east England and East Anglia in particular were now densely populated, while Salisbury Plain and the downs of Sussex, Dorset, Wiltshire and Berkshire (associated with the White Horse of the Ridgeway above Uffington) were probably cultivated throughout the Roman occupation, when the population of Britain rose to between half and one-and-a-half million. The Romans also began to settle the fens in

Cambridgeshire and Lincolnshire, embarking on extensive drainage projects, including the construction of the seventy miles long Car dyke in Lincolnshire. But while cultivation was fairly extensive on the southern chalklands most of the lowlands, notably the Weald and the Midland Plain, were still covered with oak forest. The latter was mainly uninhabited and probably penetrated deeply only by hunters in quest of the numerous deer, wolves and bears, though the Romans smelted iron on a large scale in such localities as the Weald of Kent and the Forest of Dean, burning oak, ash, birch and hazel in order to obtain charcoal for this purpose.

Cultivation of the chalk ridges and the summits of the downs almost ceased after the Romano-Celtic occupation, and when the Legions finally evacuated Britain in AD 410 rural areas gradually lapsed into their former primeval state, and the population of Britain remained static for the next six or seven hundred years. Nor initially did the Anglo-Saxons recultivate, though draining some areas of marshland for sheep-grazing. Nevertheless, it was the Saxons, from the fifth century, who, by their extensive felling of the valley woodlands to clear ground for their open-field cultivation with eight-ox ploughs, transformed England from a largely forested country into an extensively pastoral one, though considerable tracts were to remain under forest for another thousand years. But even the Saxons confined their clearing operations to the lighter forest, for the waterlogged jungles on the heavy clay land probably harboured a much more dangerous animal than any wolf or bear. This was the anopheline mosquito, the vector of the ague or malaria, which was still prevalent in the fens of East Anglia and Sedgemoor as late as 1870. Just as the tsetse fly has preserved sanctuaries for the big game in some parts of Africa, so *anopheles* may have delayed the extermination of the larger carnivores in Britain.

Forest laws relating to the hunting and control of game and predators in Britain can be traced back to the second century BC, when Dornadilla or Dovadil, fourth king of the Scots, decreed that any man killing a wolf should receive an ox. In England the oldest forest laws appear to be those promulgated by King Ine of Wessex at the end of the seventh century AD, while in Wales the three recensions of Hywel Dda's 'Forest Laws of Cambria' came into force before the middle of the tenth century. The purpose of these laws was not only to control the numbers of wolves and other predators that killed livestock, and those of the deer that ate the crops, but also, paradoxically, to conserve the herds of deer which, since there was but the barest minimum of fodder for over-wintering essential breeding livestock, represented an important source of fresh meat for much of the year. However, although by the eleventh century Britain's original forty million acres of forest had been reduced to about ten million, the Saxons' deforestation was of a temporary nature, for under the Normans there was a large-scale and systematic devastation of crop-lands, cleared for royal hunting forests, within which most cultivation was prohibited under pain of ferocious penalties – those enforced by Canute being even harsher than William's:

> Husbandmen, with their harmless herds and flocks, are driven from their well-cultivated fields, their meadows, and their pastures, that wild beasts may range in them without interruption [wrote John of Salisbury]. If one of these great and merciless hunters shall pass by your habitation, bring forth hastily all the refreshment you have in your house, or that you can readily buy, or borrow from your neighbours; and that you may not be involved in ruin, or even accused of treason.

Henry II, Richard and John all increased the acreage of the royal forests which, however, included such heaths and moors as the New Forest, Dartmoor and the Peak, together with large tracts of land too poor to offer more than a bare subsistence living, despite John Manwood's affirmation that:

> By the new afforestations of these three foresayd Kings the Forests in everie place were so much enlarged, that the greatest part of this Realme was become Forest, to the great griefe and sorrow of the inhabitants of this land: for by reason that the boundage of the Forest was then so great, and the Laws so sharpe and cruelle, that it was almost impossible for any man, that was dwelling or abiding within the limits and bounds of the Forest to live without the daunger thereof.

Moreover, the compulsory 'fallowing' within the hunting pale of previously cultivated land resulted in its recolonisation by natural vegetation, so that by the middle of the twelfth century it is possible that one-third of England comprised royal 'forest'. This extended almost to the gates of London, for in his *Life* of Thomas à Becket, written in 1174, William Fitz-Stephen, a monk of Canterbury, stated that on the north side of the City were open meadows of pasture land, and beyond these 'an immense forest, woody ranges, hiding places of wild beasts, of stags, of fallow deer, of boars, and of forest bulls (*Tauri sylvestres*)'.

However, in the latter stages of that century there was a reversion to arable farming and pasture, with the Cistercians opening up vast sheepwalks, not only in southern Scotland and on the eastern slopes of the Pennines, but also on the Cotswolds and other south country hills; and sheep, effectually preventing the regeneration of woodland, were also to denude the Lakeland fells. By the middle of the thirteenth century the eight million sheep in Britain outnumbered the human population by more than two to one, and timber had become so scarce in north-east England that it had to be imported from Scandinavia.

During the Tudor period the human population increased to some four and a half million, having recovered from the 30 or 40 per cent mortality resulting from the ravages of the Black Death – the bubonic plague spread by one of man's accidental imports to Britain, the black rat; and deforestation continued, with the introduction of sheep-farming to lower ground in the Midlands, with clearances for corn, and with the felling of timber for utensils, tools and construction purposes, until an Act of Parliament in 1503 could declare the forests of England to be 'utterly destroyed'. Since the browsing and trampling of stock prevented the growth of seedlings, the woods degenerated into rough grasslands or heaths interspersed with brush scrub such as hawthorn and gorse, which could resist the attacks of browsing animals (goats and donkeys excepted), and are still characteristic of many commons.

Against this background we can now enquire into the fate of those mammals that failed to survive in Britain until the present day.

3 Why Did They Become Extinct?

Elks

We know, from their various remains in caves and particularly in the black silt or white marl underlying peatbogs, that the giant Irish elk, so-called, survived until after the final glaciation and perhaps until early in the Middle Stone Age. Despite their eleven or twelve feet spread of palmate antlers, weighing from seventy to one hundred pounds, these great deer were apparently more nearly related to red deer than to elk; nor were they confined to Ireland, being present not only in England and Wales and at least as far north as southern Perthshire, but also widely distributed throughout Europe. Although their bones often lie crowded together in what were once swamps or shallow lakes, as if the animals had been driven into them, and although such a monstrous deer would have provided sumptuous meals for a tribe of Stone Age hunters, there is in fact no evidence that man had colonised Ireland prior to the Mesolithic era. We can only speculate that the deer succumbed, not to over-hunting, but to modifications of their habitat, consequent upon the post-glacial climatic change, which resulted in their being unable to obtain sufficient nutritious provender to compensate for their excessive antler growth. Indeed, since they were fine-boned, their actual body-weight was probably less than that of the true elk or moose, which may scale 1,800 pounds and stand 7½ feet at the shoulder.

Remains of the latter occur frequently in such Mesolithic settlements as that at Star Carr, though they were only occasionally portrayed by the Magdalenian artists; and they may have survived in England until the Iron Age and possibly up to the time of the Roman occupation. In Scotland their relics have been found from the Borders (especially in the valley of the Tweed and the Solway Firth) to the north of Sutherland; and three Gaelic names – *os, miol and lòn* – recall the 'great dark deer of swift yet shambling gait' that inhabited the northern Highlands when the defensive brochs, whose massive circular stone towers had controlled the seaways' approaches since the Iron Age,

6. A Young Moose

were still in use in the tenth century. Some may have indeed remained until about 1300, for they are remembered in such legends and poems, based on oral traditions, as the *Bas Dhiarmid* (*The Death of Dermid*). that includes the lines –

> Glen Shee, that glen by my side
> Where oft is heard the voice of deer and elk –

while another poem, *Miann 'a bhaird aosda (The Aged Bard's Wish)* composed not later than the eighteenth century, contains the verse:

> I see the ridge of hinds, the steep of the sloping glen,
> The wood of cuckoos at its foot,
> The blue height of a thousand pines
> Of wolves, and roes, and elks.

What factor can have brought about the extinction of the elk at such an early date in England? Over-hunting can hardly have done so, nor predation, though no doubt wolves took their toll of the calves, as might bears and lynxes. But as in the case of the giant deer, alterations in their habitat were probably responsible. England's countless marshes and meres should have provided them with an ideal environment; but it will be recalled that during the Iron Age large areas of pine wood had been overwhelmed by bog and swamp, as other tracts had earlier been replaced by oak woods. Now, while the elks' favourite food is lake plants, particularly water-lilies for which they wade belly-deep and of which they may nearly denude a lake, they are dependent in winter not

. An Elk

only on the buds, twigs and bark of bog willow and aspens, but to a greater extent on those of young conifers. These they can browse to a height of fourteen feet when elevated on hard-trodden ramps of snow, or, by running their chins up and along the branches, bend them down from a height of twenty feet and strip their foliage. It is significant that throughout their Eurasian range elk are the most widely distributed fauna in the coniferous forests of the endless *taiga*. Sweden indeed, relative to its size, boasts a larger population of elk than does Canada, and despite an annual hunting kill of twenty or thirty thousand, their numbers are actually increasing.

Reindeer

Reindeer were a major quarry of the Old Stone Age peoples, and Pleistocene remains of them have been located in Scotland from the Solway Firth to Caithness and also on Rousay in the Orkneys. Yet there have been no Neolithic finds of reindeer in Britain, despite the fact that they were being domesticated on the Continent at that time, and they were extinct in Ireland before the arrival of man. Moreover, although a few Iron Age antler fragments have been recovered in Sutherland, the Picts, who were contemporary with the Romans and were prolific carvers in stone of such animals as wolves, stags and domestic bulls and horses, and also of wild geese and salmon, have left no record of reindeer. Possibly a warm inter-glacial period destroyed the Pleistocene reindeer's specialised tundra food of lichens, and a fresh stock subsequently entered Britain. As the ice-sheet receded, so the new herds of reindeer followed the tundra to the moors of north Britain, on which grew their winter feed of *Cladonia* and *Usnea* lichens and summer feed of sedges and grasses, though the true 'reindeer moss' did not thrive as profusely in Britain as in Lapland. According to the evidence, for what it is worth, of the *Orkneyinga Saga*, it was the custom about 1159 for two Norse jarls of Orkney 'to go over nearly every summer (*aestate*) into Caithness and then up into the woods to hunt Red Deer or Reins'. *Aestate* in fact probably signifies autumn, for antlers recovered from the jarls' burial places have been clean of velvet, which they would not have been until mid-September. Some reindeer might have survived in north Scotland as a forest type until after the twelfth century but for hunting and forest clearance – though wolves must have preyed heavily on them too – for the reference to hunting them in the woods, together with evidence provided by the Cromagnons' paintings, suggests that some European reindeer were, like the woodland caribou of Canada, forest animals. Although Mesolithic man did not reach Scotland until about 8000 BP, woods were being felled to provide fuel for smelting as early as the Bronze and Iron Ages, and this practice was continued by the Roman legionaries, though the Picts, employing guerrilla tactics from their mountain strongholds, prevented the Romans from occupying the interior of the Highlands. Subsequently those Norsemen based in Orkney and Iceland plundered the

6. Reindeer

forests of the western Highlands for timber for shipbuilding, and the Vikings were intermittently burning the Forest of Caledon in the central Highlands from the ninth to the twelfth centuries.

But the reindeer have now returned to Scotland, to browse the lichens on the moors and hills, the young leaves of the birches and the early spring grass in the glens, and the forest agarics; for, after a number of haphazard attempts to re-introduce them in the nineteenth century, a series of importations of domesticated stock from Swedish Lapland and southern Norway during the years 1952 to 1961 has finally resulted in the formation of a herd of eighty or so in a suitable habitat of 5,000 acres in the Cairngorms, extending from the shores of Loch Morlich to the 4,000-foot summits of Cairn Gorm and Cairn Lochan. More than three hundred have now been bred in the Cairngorms, and of the present herd only one – a bull born at Whipsnade from a Russian cow – is not home-bred.

Wild Horses

As in the case of the reindeer so, too, the wild horses of the Pleistocene apparently failed to survive in Britain, for no Mesolithic or Neolithic remains have been found of these ponies and there is no evidence that horses were domesticated in Britain before the Bronze Age. That wild horses did, however, re-enter Britain does not rest solely on ancient traditions associated with the Exmoor, Dartmoor and Fell breeds, but on the presence in the Highlands within historic times of wild, as opposed to feral ponies, distinguished by the absence of ergots or fetlock callosities and also of 'chestnuts' on the inner side of the hind legs. Hector Boece or Boethius mentioned them in his *Scotorum Historae* of 1526, and John Taylor the water poet – since he was by profession a waterman on the Thames – referred in 1618 to 'deere, wilde horses, wolves' on the Braes of Mar. Moreover, in the opinion of some authorities the original pure-bred Exmoor pony and the larger Devon pack-horse (now extinct) were truer examples of a wild horse than the tarpan of doubtful ancestry, and as genuine as the central Asian Przewalski's horse, of which, according to current reports by Mongolian zoologists, upwards of fifty still survive in Dzungaria. Whatever may have been their origin, the tarpans – of which there are said to have been a grey steppe breed and possibly a smaller forest breed – still ranged across the steppes from Poland in the west to Lake Baikal in the east as late as the eighteenth century, and were quite numerous in the Ukraine during the first half of the nineteenth century; but as a result of the ever-increasing agricultural exploitation of the steppes and the slaughter by farmers of the tarpan stallions, which frequently attacked domestic stallions when abducting their mares, the last of these 'wild' horses were exterminated towards the end of the 1870s, though one survived in captivity until 1918 or 1919.

Aurochsen

Although the Rune Song, probably the oldest extant English poem, states that:

> The aurochs is proud and extravagantly horned;
> A very fierce beast, it fights with its horns.
> Marching mightily across the moors,
> It is a most courageous beast –

the author must have been writing from experience on the Continent, where the aurochsen ranged from Spain to southern Sweden, and from France to the Near East and central Asia, for they apparently became extinct in Britain at least 2,500 years ago during the Bronze or early Iron Age, though since their skulls have been recovered from Pictish brochs in Caithness it is possible that some survived until the ninth or tenth century AD. It is, again, difficult to account for their early extinction, for though we know that they were hunted in East Anglia by Neolithic men it is not credible that the relatively few Bronze or Iron Age hunters were numerous enough to exterminate them – certainly not in north Britain where their remains are most numerous – particularly since they survived in the wild state in central Europe until the fifteenth century or later. Nor should the limited destruction of forest and the moderate climatic changes during the sub-Atlantic phase have affected them so adversely, though it is true that their ideal environment appears to have been one with a climate less cold than that in which the European bison thrived. It is perhaps significant that they are portrayed only in the later cave paintings, dating from about 15,000 BP and may not therefore have migrated into Europe until the climate was warming up in the pre-Boreal phase.

One of the earliest writers to mention the aurochs – or *urus*, as it was known until the general use of Latin was relinquished in the

Middle Ages – was Julius Caesar in his *de Bello Gallico*, in which he was careful to distinguish between the aurochs and the bison, which was never a native of Britain. It has been suggested that he would certainly have commented on the former had they been present in southern Britain at the time of his invasions, but in view of the briefness of these there seems no reason why he should. Of the aurochsen in the immense German Hercynian forest lying north of the Danube he wrote:

> It is known that many kinds of wild beasts not seen in any other places breed therein, of which the following are those that differ most from the rest of the animal world and appear worthy of record . . . A third species consists of the ure-oxen so called. In size these are smaller than elephants; in appearance, colour and shape they are as bulls. Great is their strength and great their speed, and they spare neither man nor beast once sighted. These the Germans slay zealously, by taking them in pits; by such work the young men harden themselves and by this kind of hunting train themselves, and those who have slain most of them bring the horns with them to a public place for a testimony thereof, and win great renown. But even if they are caught very young, the animals cannot be tamed or accustomed to human beings. In bulk, shape and appearance their horns are very different from the horns of our oxen. The natives collect them zealously and encase the edges with silver, and then at their grandest banquets use them as drinking-cups.

From the cave paintings at Lascaux, together with such medieval objects as a silver vase from Maikop in the northern Caucasus, and gold figurines from other parts of Russia, and a painting at Augsburg in Germany, we know that, though they varied considerably in size from one region to another, the bulls of these great cattle might stand more than six feet at their humped shoulders and weigh around 2,000 pounds. Although the sixteenth-century Swiss naturalist, Conrad Gesner, described their horns as being rather slim and curving forward (like those of the Camargue fighting bulls), he also referred to aurochs horns six feet long in Strasbourg Cathedral, while the great drinking horn, presumably that of an aurochs, recovered from the early seventh-century Sutton Hoo ship burial in Suffolk, measured nine inches across the mouth. The black bulls were, typically, long-legged and deep-chested with curly hair on their foreheads, white or greyish muzzles and a white or yellow stripe along the spine, while the much smaller cows were dun-coloured or red with darker heads, necks and legs, and the calves fawn, darkening to the adult colour by the time they were about two years old, though male calves did not acquire the deepest black of the master bulls for several years.

As early as the Merovingian period (500-751) the aurochsen had already become so scarce over much of France that hunting them was a

Royal prerogative, though they remained plentiful in the wilder forests of the Vosges until the twelfth century, and were still present in Prussia in the thirteenth century and in Lithuania in the early fifteenth; but by Gesner's time the few surviving aurochsen were mainly confined to parks, for by 1565 the last remaining herd of some thirty beasts had been gathered into the Jaktovowka game reserve in Poland. Although no hunting was allowed in the reserve, poachers had reduced the herd to four by 1602, and by 1620 to one aged cow that survived for a further seven years – the last of her kind. However, in the 1920s and again in the 1950s successful attempts were made to recreate the aurochs by crossing breeds of modern cattle that exhibited certain of its characteristics. In the first experiment Hungarian and Podalian steppe cattle, West Highland cattle, grey and brown Alpine breeds, piebald Friesians and Corsicans were crossed; in the second experiment Spanish fighting cattle, Camargue cattle and the Corsicans. In both experiments typical aurochsen were eventually bred and continued to breed true to type and, what is perhaps more remarkable, these not only resembled the aurochs physically in conformation, colour and agility, but also in being fierce and temperamental.

'Wild' Cattle

Was there any aurochs blood in the numerous herds of 'wild' cattle at large in the forests of Britain until the Middle Ages, or were these feral escapes from domestic herds? It is generally held that up to the time of the Roman invasion of Britain the only cattle with which the aurochsen bulls might have mated and produced crosses were the small, almost deer-like Celtic shorthorns, which were also dark-coloured; but if that

7. A Modern Reconstruction of an Aurochs

was the case, did the Druids, who were sacrificing white bulls long before the arrival of the Romans, obtain them from their co-religionists in Gaul? Subsequently the Romans may themselves have introduced white cattle with long *urus*-type horns for sacrificial purposes, while the post-Roman invaders, who drove the Celtic herdsmen into west Britain, certainly brought with them red *urus*-type cattle from west Germany. Determining the origins of the wild herds is made more difficult by the fact that they appear to have included more than one kind of cattle. It will be recalled that Fitz-Stephen referred to *Tauri sylvestres* in Enfield Chase, and Canute's 'Forest Laws' stated that: 'There are also a great number of cattle, which, although they live within the limits of the Forest . . . nevertheless cannot at all be reputed beasts of the forest as wild horse, *bubali*, wild cows, and the like.' In his *Lives of the Abbots of St Albans* the Benedictine Matthew Paris, the most reliable of the medieval chroniclers, also stated that in the days of Edward the Confessor: 'There abounded throughout the whole of Cietria [the Chilterns] spacious woods, thick and large, the habitation of numerous and various beasts, wolves, boars, forest bulls (*Tauri sylvestres*) and stags.' But there is no indication as to what these English wild cattle were like. Had they been notably distinctive – pure white in colour for example – such peculiarities would surely have been mentioned, as was the case in Wales and Scotland. Hywel Dda's 'Forest Laws', for instance, included a provision that the King of Aberfraw in Anglesey was to be compensated for injury by the payment of one hundred cows for each hundred townships and 'a white bull with red ears to each hundred cows'. Although in Wales some of these white cattle were domesticated they nevertheless retained wild characteristics, since they were grazed on the mountains because they were the only breed that would fight off wolves; though once the wolves had been exterminated, the cattle were replaced by sheep, for they made poor butchers' beasts, weighing only five hundredweight at six years of age and eight hundredweight when finally mature. However, 'wild' cattle were still being hunted on the hills of Pembroke during Elizabeth's reign, though there is no mention of them in Radnor Forest after about 1560. They were indeed hunted as beasts of the chase throughout Britain and, whether genuinely wild or feral or partly domesticated, exhibited the fierceness characteristic of the aurochsen, as illustrated by Boece's description of them in the Tor Wood near Stirling, then one of the largest of the remaining tracts of forest in Scotland:

> In the Tor Wood was sometimes white bulls with crisp and curland manes, like fierce lions; and though they seemed meak and tame in the remanent figure of their bodies, they were more wild than any other beasts, and had such hatred against the company and society of men, that they came never in the woods, nor leisured where they found any feet or hand thereof; and many days after, they ate nothing of the herbs that were twitched or handled by men. Their

> bulls were so wild, that they were never taken but sleight and crafty labour: and so impatient that, after their taking, they died for insupportable dolour. As soon as any man invaded their bulls, they rushed into so terrible press on him, that they dang him to the earth taking no fear of hounds, sharp lances, nor other most penetrative weapons.

Boece's use of the word 'sometimes' suggests that these white cattle were no longer to be found in the wild state in Scotland at the beginning of the sixteenth century, and Bishop Leslie of Rosse, writing in 1578, also stated that: 'He was afortymes a frequent beast in this Torr Wood, but now consumed through the gluttony of men only in three places is left, in the Park of Striviling [Stirling], the wood of Cummirnalde [Cumbernauld] and of Kincairne [Kincardine].' The Cumbernauld forest was linked by the Tor Wood to the Forest of Caledon, which at that time stretched from Glen Lyon and Rannoch to Strathspey and Strathglass, and from Glencoe east to the Braes of Mar, though the use of the term 'forest' in Scotland has always included tracts of open moorland, as in the modern deer forest. Herds of white cattle were indeed impounded in parks in many parts of Britain, including Cadzow in Lanarkshire, Chartley in Staffordshire, Dynevor in Carmarthenshire and Chillingham in Northumberland, though as late as the 1830s John Colquhoun encountered what he described in *The Moor and The Loch* as a domestic herd of white cattle grazing the verges of a moorland road in Argyllshire. It is significant that nearly all these parks were in localities famed for their wild cattle. The Tankervilles' estate of Chillingham lies, for example, hard by Chatton, which was a royal hunting domain with wild cattle as long ago as 1292, and the Chillingham park herd has apparently existed without a break since that year in its sanctuary of steep bracken-covered hills, rough pastures and woodlands, and at the present time numbers upwards of fifty; but though blood-group experts attest to the purity of these cattle, it is difficult to believe that the herd can in fact have survived for seven centuries without some infusions of new blood, either deliberate or on those occasions when the park pale has been breached or has fallen into disrepair. But it is remarkable that throughout this long occupation the Chillingham cattle have never become fully domesticated, not only retaining their wild social structure, with the bulls fighting for the herd leadership, but also their ancient antipathy towards man and his scent. Calving cows, which retreat to the most secluded places to give birth and do not introduce their calves to the herd for three or four days, are particularly savage. However, this trait has been exaggerated. There does not appear to be any record of an unprovoked attack on man, and an early Lord Tankerville, after stating that they hide their calves and feed at night, added that:

> They are fierce when pressed, but generally speaking very timorous,

> moving off on the appearance of anyone even at a great distance . . . On the other hand, in winter, when coming down for food . . . and being in constant contact with people, they will let you almost come among them, particularly if on horseback.

His lordship also stated that: 'They are bad breeders, and are much subject to the "rash" – a complaint common to animals bred in-and-in.' Nevertheless, they have retained an immunity to many of the diseases afflicting modern breeds of cattle, though physically they have degenerated with prolonged in-breeding to what can only be described as rather poor likenesses of the Ayrshire breed. It has been asserted that the Chillingham herd has bred true down the centuries, retaining the white colour and distinctive points of black-tipped horns and reddish hair inside the ears – Hywel Dda's bulls with red ears – whereas herds in other parks throw occasional red or black calves; but this is not strictly correct, for at the end of the seventeenth century there were more individuals with black ear-hair than red.

4 Beavers and Wild Boar Remembered

Beavers

Britain is studded from southern England to the Fens, Wales and Scotland with place-names derived from the various terms for a beaver, as for example Beverege in Worcestershire, Bevercotes in Nottinghamshire, Beverstone in Gloucestershire and Beversbrook in Wiltshire, while in Anglo-Saxon days the Yorkshire town of Beverley was known as Beorforleag or the Beaver's Lea. In Wales the Llyn-yr-Afangc pool on

8. A Beaver Carrying a Stick to its Dam

the Conway is the Beaver's Pool, and Welsh and Scottish place-names may be very similar, as in the case of Llostlydan and Losleathan for Broad-Tail. Yet despite this abundance of place-names there is no literary reference to beavers prior to Hywel Dda's 'Forest Laws', and there is no mention of them in Domesday Book. Beaver fur – and also that of marten and ermine – was used as trimmings on the robes of royalty, and any pelt was the property of the king; and since in Hywel Dda's time the price of a beaver pelt was 120 pence, whereas a marten's was 24 pence, an otter's 12 pence, and those of wolves and foxes only 8 pence apiece, beavers may already have been becoming scarce as early as the tenth century. They had certainly been almost exterminated by the twelfth century, for in 1188 Gerald de Barri, alias Giraldus Cambrensis – a member of the Norman and Welsh nobility, who held high positions at the English court – when travelling through Cardiganshire with the Archbishop of Canterbury, observed that the Teifi was the only river in Wales in which beavers were to be found, and that there were none in England; and though the fourteenth-century poet Dafydd ap Gwilym writes as if he had himself watched beavers, there is no factual mention of them in Wales after Giraldus, and it was his long, partly legendary and mythical, but also apparently in part first-hand account of their habits that was the source of some lines in Michael Drayton's learned nonsense, *Polyolbion*, composed early in the seventeenth century:

> More famous long agone, than for the salmon's leap,
> For *beavers* Tivy was, in her strong banks that bred.

Giraldus' account is too fascinating to be omitted:

> The beavers, in order to construct their castle in the middle of rivers, make use of the animals of their own species instead of carts . . . Some of them . . . receive on their bellies the logs of wood cut off by their associates, which they hold tight with their feet, and thus with transverse pieces placed in their mouths, are drawn along backwards, with their cargo, by other beavers, who fasten themselves with their teeth to the raft . . . In some deep and still corner of the river, the beavers . . . entwine the branches of willow with other wood, and different kinds of leaves, to the usual height of the water, and having made withinside a communication from floor to floor, they elevate a kind of stage, or scaffold, from which they may observe and watch the rising of the waters . . . The beaver has but four teeth, two above, and two below, which being broad and sharp, cut like a carpenter's axe, and as such he uses them. They make excavations and dry hiding places in the banks near their dwellings, and when they hear the stroke of the hunter, who with sharp poles endeavours to penetrate them, they fly as soon as possible to the

> defence of their castle . . . When the beaver finds he cannot save himself from the . . . dogs who follow him . . . he throws away that, which . . . he knows to be the object sought for, and . . . castrates himself, from which circumstance he has gained the name of Castor; and if . . . the dogs should chase an animal which had previously been castrated, he has the sagacity to run to an elevated spot, and there lifting his leg, shews the hunter that the object of his pursuit is gone . . . The beavers have broad, short tails, thick, like the palm of a hand, which they use as a rudder in swimming . . . this part . . . is without hair, and smooth.

During his earlier travels through Ireland in 1183 and 1185-6 Giraldus had also noted that there were no beavers in that country, and that they were rare in Scotland; but they may have survived in Scotland until the sixteenth century, for though not mentioned in the game laws of the previous century, Boece refers to 'incomparable numbers' in the vicinity of Loch Ness. It is true that Boece cannot be relied upon implicitly, but this statement seems to be confirmed by the fact that German traders were calling at Inverness about that time to purchase beaver skins.

Giraldus' account of the beaver on the Teifi suggests that British beavers, unlike most of their kin throughout Europe but like the majority in North America, constructed dams across streams to form ponds or lakes in which they could build dwelling lodges of stones and branches cemented with mud. Because they feed mainly on the tender inner bark from the higher branches of sapling trees – virtually the only food available during the winter months – the deforestation of the banks of lowland rivers may have contributed to their extinction in Britain, for since on land they can only gallop clumsily at the pace of a man's slow run, they are defenceless against predators and will not, therefore, venture much more than two hundred yards from their pond or bank refuge. Thus, whether they build lodges in dammed ponds, for which branches are required, or occupy burrows in river banks, they cannot survive without an easily accessible supply of trees.

In Europe the beaver may excavate tunnels up to fifty feet long in the steep banks of large rivers. These river burrows are provided with one or more underwater entrances, which are sited deep enough to ensure that their owners can emerge below water if the river freezes over in a hard winter. European beavers – whose habitat was mainly coniferous forest, in contrast to the American beavers' preference for deciduous woods – had also been almost exterminated by the eighteenth century, with only scattered colonies surviving on the Elbe and the Rhone and in remote districts of Norway: but they have recently been successfully re-introduced to Switzerland after an interval of 250 years, and also to Finland and Sweden in large numbers. Thus there is no reason why they should not be re-introduced to Britain if a suitable habitat could be found for them. Indeed beavers imported from Canada and France to the Isle of Bute in the late nineteenth century thrived initially, though the colony died out within fifteen years, while another colony planted in a locality in Sussex about the same time survived for nearly sixty years until 1948.

Wild Boars

That Britain also abounds with place-names attributable to the wild boar is not surprising, since from the earliest times it was the foremost beast of the chase:

> On his bow-back he hath a battle set
> Of bristly pikes, that ever threat his foes;
> His eyes like glowworms shine when he doth fret;
> His snout digs sepulchres where'er he goes;
> Being mov'd, he strikes what'er is in his way,
> And when he strikes his crooked tushes slay.
>
> *Venus and Adonis*

In addition to numerous Gaelic place references to boars in the Highlands there are such well-known examples in England as Boarshill in Oxfordshire, Boarhunt in Hampshire, Boarsford in Herefordshire, Wild Boar Clough in Cheshire and Wild Boar Fell in the Lake District, while both Eversham and Everley are derived from the Saxon word for boar – *eofor.*

Among the Celtic chieftains the hunting of the boar was imbued with an almost religious prestige, exceeding that of the nineteenth-century fox-hunter for his chase. Boars were portrayed on Celtic monumental stones and on the standards of the Roman legions. A sculpture at Ribchester, for example, featured a boar on one side and on the other the motto of the XXth Legion, which was stationed at Caerleon-on-Usk; while an altar in County Durham was dedicated to the god Sylvanus in thanksgiving for the killing of a huge boar. Medieval followers of the chase displayed a proper knowledge of the habits of their quarry, in so far as these bore upon the actual hunting of them, and the *Booke of Hunting or The Noble Art of Venerie* produced in 1575 by George Turbevile, a gentleman of Dorset, includes an acute account of the wild boar – though admittedly most of this was derived from a French book published fourteen years earlier:

> The difference between the wild swine and our hog is great. . . First they are commonly blacke, or grisled, or streaked with blacke, whereas ours are white, sanded, and of all colours . . . the wylde swyne in their gate do always set the hinder foote within the fore foot, or very neare, and stay themselves more upon the toe than upon the heele, shutting their claws before close: and commonly, they strike their gards (which are their dew claws) upon the ground, the which sway outwards: and the sides of their hoofs do cut and

9. A Wild Boar

pare the ground, the which our swine do not, for they spread and open their fore claws leaving the ground between them: and they be commonly round and worne, leaving and staying more upon the heele, than upon the toe. Againe, they set not their hinder foote within their fore foot, and their gards fall straight upon the ground, and never shoyle or leane outwards: and they beat down and soile the ground and cut it not. Also the soale of their feete is fleshy, and maketh no plaine print upon the ground as the wild swine do. There is likewise great difference in their rowtings: for a wild swine doth rowt deeper, because his snout is longer: and when they come into corne fields they follow a furrow, rowting and worming all along by some balke until they come to the end. But tame swine rowte here and there all about the field, and never follow their rowting as the wild swine do. Likewise you may know them by the difference in their feedings in corne growne: for, the wild swine beare down the corne round about them in one certaine place, and tame swine feede scattering here and there.

To some extent wild boars were conserved: 'Doth the wild boar feed in the old frank?' asks Prince Henry in *Henry IV, Part II,* referring, according to Anthony Dent's *Lost Beasts of Britain,* to the fact that after the winter supply of acorns, beechmast and chestnuts had been exhausted in the forest, food for the wild swine was put out in franks or pens, which were divided into stalls to prevent the largest or most aggressive boars from bullying the others and gobbling up all the food. This practice had been customary in Strathmore (Forfarshire) as early as the thirteenth century.

References to boar-hunting decrease during Elizabeth's reign, with the progressive destruction of oak woods to fuel the bloomeries – the charcoal-burning furnaces in which iron-ore was smelted; and although wild boars were being hunted in Windsor Park as late as James I's reign, they were becoming scarce and much interbred with domestic swine, and Charles I was obliged to import wild stock from France to the New Forest, where, according to the diarist John Aubrey, they 'became terrible to the travellers'. The wild stock finally became extinct both in England and Scotland during the seventeeth century, partly as a result of hunting and partly by absorption into domestic herds, though imported boars could be shot in the New Forest at the end of the nineteenth century, while the killing of one on a forestry road near Nairn in the Scottish Highlands in 1976 has yet to be explained.

During the eighteenth century some domestic piglets were still being born with the horizontal stripes of their wild ancestors, while a century later both in the Highlands and on the Welsh hills gaunt, long-legged, semi-domesticated swine with very long snouts, a ruff of coarse bristles round the neck, and a pronounced ridge of coarse bristles along the spine, were running wild on the moors and invading the corn and potato fields. According to a Welsh description in 1872: 'They can only be resembled to an alligator mounted upon stilts, having bristles instead of scales . . . Their length of leg might possibly enable them to compete with a greyhound.'

Although wild boars are generally held to have become extinct in Ireland in prehistoric times, an old Irish tract, possibly as old as AD 650, asks ironically: 'Who, for instance, would bring wolves, deer, and *wood pigs,* and foxes, badgers, and little hares . . . to Ireland?'; while Giraldus reported that: 'In no part of the world have I seen such an abundance of boars and forest hogs; but they are a small, ill-shaped, and cowardly breed, no less degenerate in boldness and ferocity than in their growth and shape.'

In Europe their range has never extended further north than southern Scandinavia, possibly because they cannot winter in regions where the snowfall is much more than two feet, which is presumably the maximum depth through which they can obtain roots, bulbs and tubers. 'The wild boar is a common beast enough and there be few gentlemen who have not seen some of them,' wrote Gaston de Foix (Gaston Phoebus) in his *La Livre de la Chace* in 1391, a year or two before he was either killed in a bear hunt or died of apoplexy after one; but though boars still inhabit most of the great European forests, particularly in those parts where there is thick underbrush and bog, their numbers have been much reduced in the more populated regions, and their survival must be linked with the fecundity of the sows, which are capable of producing two litters of a dozen annually.

5 The Last of the Big Predators

Lynxes

Three big predators have also become extinct in Britain. There are no Celtic or old English names for the lynx, which seems never to have established itself in numbers, and is generally considered to have become extinct in Neolithic times. The remains of only one have been found in a limestone cave at Inchnadamph in Sutherland, which also contained the bones of northern rat-voles and arctic lemmings, whose habitats may have been destroyed by rising temperatures and forest growth. Yet the lynxes' prey must have abounded, for they included not only their favourite mountain hares but also roe deer, young red deer and possibly young elk (though a large lynx weighs only sixty pounds), small rodents, foxes, wild cats and badgers, together with such birds as grouse, ptarmigan and duck, and also fish. Possibly the regular cyclical lows in the numbers of hares contributed to the lynxes' extinction within the limited area of these islands, for there is some evidence that after a crash in the hare population a lynx may ignore other forms of prey. Also to be taken into account is the fact that young lynxes mature rather slowly and are dependent on the female for most of their first year, for at nine months they still retain their milk teeth and their claws are still undeveloped, so that they are unable to kill even hares. However, in the more spacious and wilder expanses of western Europe they were able to survive in woods and forests from Scandinavia to the Mediterranean until quite recently, but because of the value of their fur and their alleged destructiveness to domestic stock have now been exterminated in all regions except Scandinavia and Spain and possibly the Pyrenees, where they have been able to adapt to life in mountainous areas, providing that these include rocky outcrops and ravines in which to lair and rear their cubs.

Brown Bears

There is no mystery attached to the extinction of brown bears in Britain. Though in the main harmless to man and his livestock, being vegetarians rather than carnivores, they were considered dangerous beasts; moreover, every hunter wanted to kill a bear, and still does so in those parts of western Europe where a few survive. The Belgae may have hunted them with their mastiffs, and they must have been quite numerous at one time, for their skins were exported. The poet Martial mentions that large numbers of bears from Caledonia were transported to the Imperial Circus in Rome, and according to Bishop Leslie the Forest of Caledon was formerly extremely full (*refertissimam*) of bears. They certainly survived in England until the eighth century, since in 750 Archbishop Egbert ordained in his *Penitentiale* that.

> If anyone shall hit a deer or other animal with an arrow and it escapes and is found dead three days afterwards, and if a dog, a wolf, a fox or a bear, or any other wild beast hath begun to feed on it, no Christian shall touch it.

Bears also feature on the tenth-century hog-stones in Yorkshire and Durham. In Scotland they may have survived later than in England, but there is no evidence of their presence in Ireland within historic times, and no mention of them in Wales in Hywel Dda's 'Laws' though *Y Naw Helwriaeth* (*The Nine Huntings*) refers to bear as the best venison in the world, adding that: 'When it is killed, it is not much chased because it can walk but slowly and then it need only be walked off its legs and bayed at and at last killed.' Although the earliest known manuscript of *Y Naw Helwriaeth* dates from about 1560, its origins are obviously much earlier. Thomas Pennant attributed it to Prince Gryffyd ap Cynan in the late eleventh century, and its style recalls Edward, Duke of York's early-fifteenth-century *The Master of Game*, which, though the oldest treatise on the Chase in English, was an almost literal translation of Gaston de Foix's *La Livre de la Chace,* with the addition of five original chapters. Whether the presence of bears in Wales is indicated by such place-names as Penarth is disputed. According to some authorities *arth* refers either to a den or to a shrine of the Celtic goddess Artio or She-Bear, while to others Penarth means Bear's Head. However, Dent has suggested that bears may have been exterminated earlier in Wales than in England because they constituted a greater danger than wolves to the mountain ponies' foals which, when grazing on the hills in summer, were liable to approach bears inquisitively and be struck down.

In western Europe, where the remaining bears have retreated to the forests of the remoter mountainous regions, they prefer mixed woods of conifers and beeches or birches, associated with a rich vegetation in the ravines or on the alpine meadows above. Such terrain supplies them not only with beechmast, hazel-nuts and berries, voles, ants and insects, but also with quantities of grass. A vegetarian may, however, be compelled to become a predator either by hunger or by being driven into

close association with relatively defenceless domestic stock, when its natural sources of food are curtailed by man's encroachment on its habitat. During the hungry season of spring, after the bears have emerged from hibernation, the only food they can obtain may be restricted to such fruits as frozen berries preserved under the snow, ants or carrion; and at this season they may infrequently attack the young of wild boars, roe or elk, and even adult elk and reindeer. But when brown bears were common in Europe they were often to be seen 'grazing' peacefully with cattle, sheep and goats in alpine meadows or among herds of reindeer on the Scandinavian fjelds.

That a very few bears have been able to survive in Europe can be attributed to their adaptability and omniverous habits and to their readiness to travel long distances in search of food. But against these favourable factors must be set the unfavourable. Theoretically, a she-bear might produce a dozen cubs in her lifetime, but the long intervals between litters render it unlikely that she will achieve this optimum; moreover, the widely-scattered nature of Europe's small communities of bears may result in some she-bears not being found by he-bears during the mating season, with the result that the interval between litters is still further extended. Whether bears can continue to exist in over-populated western Europe is problematical. In the French Alps the last was killed in 1937, and although, according to the latest reports, there are still perhaps fifty in the Pyrenees, they are constantly at risk from poisoned baits put down by shepherds. Elsewhere there are estimated to be some 250 in Scandinavia and 130 in Finland, and between 150 and 180 in the Italian Abruzzi.

Wolves

The longest surviving large predators in Britain were the wolves, which appear to have been extraordinarily numerous in every part of the country, and were so at the coming of the Romans; and were still so nine hundred years later according to the *Brut y Tywysigion,* which states that the Saxon king Edgar went into Gwynned in 962, and

> causing Iago, son of Idwal, to come to him, he imposed upon him a tribute of three hundred wolves yearly, in place of that due to him by the old law, with the liberty to kill them in any place they pleased . . . And that tribute was paid in Gwynedd for more than five and forty years, until not a wolf could be found . . . After that the King of the Saxons commuted the tribute for gold, silver and cattle, as formerly.

However, William of Malmsbury's account of this tribute is perhaps more realistic: 'He, Edgar, imposed a tribute upon the King of Wales exacting yearly three hundred wolves. This tribute continued to be paid for three years, but ceased upon the fourth, because *nullum se ulterius posse invenire professus*.'

10. A Brown Bear

To the English flock-masters of the Middle Ages wolves were, as Dent has emphasised, as terrible and feared a scourge as foot-and-mouth disease is to the stock farmers of our day. Keeping the wolf from the door or, in practice, the fold, was a hard reality and a full-time job, all and every night in addition to the shepherd's daily round. To quote Dent:

> Shepherding in wild country demanded an increased labour force; for every flock there must be three able men, armed with great hounds. But these were not the shepherds, only watchmen. The custom was (. . . we know this only from monastic records) for the watchmen to watch all night, all of them together, and sleep by day. At dawn the shepherd and his lad took over, until that hour which the French still call 'between dog and wolf' came round again. . . Other crops, other stock, come and go, but the constant factor is the flocks on the moors or the wolds or the fell.

The monk Galfrid, writing in the fourteenth century of the miracles performed by St Cuthbert seven centuries earlier, observed that marauding wolves were so numerous in Northumbria that hardly any of the richest flock-masters were able to protect their ewes and lambs, despite employing many shepherds and watchmen. Watching their flocks in the fields by night takes on a new significance in this context.

During the spring and summer months the wolves led a settled existence, rearing their three to eight cubs in dens that were usually remote from human habitation, and they did not hunt too far away from the dens; but in the autumn, when the pups were mobile at the age of six months, they became nomadic, following the deer and the domestic flocks and herds down from their summer pastures on the moors and hills in all parts of Britain. In November adults and cubs might be joined by the previous year's juveniles, and also by older animals that had failed to establish mating territories, and these packs of from half a dozen to a score of wolves would not break up until the following spring, after the February or March mating. In the *Anglo-Saxon Chronicle* January was called the *Wulf-manoth* because it was the first full month of wolf-hunting by the nobility with horse and hound:

> They go so fast when they be void that men have let them run four leashes of greyhounds, one after the other, and they could not over take him, for he runs as fast as any beast in the world, and he lasts long running, for he has a long breath.

Officially the hunting season closed on 25 March and therefore included the cubbing time when the wolves were most vulnerable and also the period when it was most profitable to hunt them, for the winter pelt was valued both as a garment and as a bed-covering –

1. A European Wolf

thought not very highly perhaps, for in Hywel Dda's time a dead wolf was worth no more than a dead fox or otter or stag. But, unofficially, both the wolf and the wild cat were the only animals to be hunted by the aristocracy yet not preserved, and wolves were shot and trapped by the foresters all the year round, in necessary disregard of the stringent Forest Laws, for the rich man's flocks were as defenceless as the poor man's swine: 'A wolf and a fox and various others which do nothing save mischief . . . it is free to slay all of them,' decreed Hywel Dda.

Although according to the eighth-century 'Ancient Laws of Ireland' wolves and also foxes, deer and herons were, improbably, kept as 'pets' in that country, it was when the wolves were in packs that they were the most feared of all wild beasts, not only in Britain but throughout Europe, though particularly in France, Spain and the Ukraine where, as in Britain, they lived in the forests or on the hills and raided the domestic stock. Before the middle of the tenth century Athelstan had erected a *hospitium* or spittal near Filey in Yorkshire as a refuge for travellers in danger of attack by wolves. 'From caterans and robbers, from wolves and all wild beasts, Lord deliver us,' beseeched the Dunkeld *Litany* in the closing years of the fifteenth century, when two ineffectual Acts were passed in Scotland for the destruction of wolves; and there were spittals throughout the Highland forests of Mar, Badenoch and Lochaber, which in Boece's time were reputed to be almost impassable because of wolves. Yet throughout these centuries, and certainly until the widespread forest clearances, deer and other wild prey abounded at all seasons of the year. Why then, when there is no reliable record of a man ever being attacked by a timber wolf in North America, were the grey wolves of Britain and Europe so feared in winter?

One cannot just dismiss this widespread fear as medieval credulity. Men must have been attacked by wolf packs, and not all such attacks can have been those of rabid wolves, though it is true that the wolf packs are decimated from time to time by outbreaks of such diseases as rabies and distemper, when they become too numerous. Since the wolves were most dangerous in winter the inference is that their attacks were impelled by hunger in hard weather, though British winters could not compare in severity with those experienced by wolves in North America. It is perhaps relevant that in their present mountain forest habitat in the Caucasus wolves are estimated to kill between 34 and 61 per cent of young boar, deer, roe, chamois and buck during the five summer months' season, yet also kill hundreds of domestic stock on the forest borders. Therefore the forest does not provide sufficient natural prey. But in winter in medieval Britain the deer would have been down in the forest, and the domestic flocks easy prey in field and fold: 'The wolfis are richt noisum to the tame bestiall in all partis of Scotland,' wrote Boece, though he qualified this statement by adding: 'except ane part thereof namit Glen Mores, in quilk the tame bestiall gettis littill damage of wild bestiall.' Since at that time Glen More embraced an enormous stretch of country extending from Argyllshire to Angus this was an inexplicable addendum. But are we to believe that the Highlanders had so diminished the deer with their spears and bows and arrows – matchlock guns were not introduced to the Highlands until 1587 – and by their *tainchels* or drives that the wolves' only source of food in winter lay in the domestic flocks and herds and in the natives themselves? It is true that red deer had been hunted in the Scottish Lowlands since the twelfth century, and that as early as 1400 an attempt was made to impose a close season, while an Act in 1474 forbade the killing of deer under one year old during storms or snow. In the sixteenth century no fewer than eleven Acts were passed for the preservation of deer, and in 1579 penalties for poaching were increased to £10 for a first offence, £20 for a second and £40 for a third, when the offender was liable to death by hanging if he was unable to pay. However, a combination of hunting and poaching, deforestation and the encroachment of immense sheep-walks hefting flocks of as many as ten thousand sheep had virtually exterminated the deer on either side of the Border by the end of the seventeenth century. But there is no evidence that there was any scarcity of deer in the vast 'forests' of the Highlands, from which more than a thousand hides were exported as late as 1614. The export of red deer and roebuck hides to Europe was indeed an important source of revenue, and may have acted as a conservation measure.

Being in packs may have emboldened the wolves, as may closer contact with man's stockyards. In France, according to Gaston de Foix, wolves were attracted to follow men by the horses they were riding and by the dead game they carried, and attacked men either because, having lost their teeth and strength in old age, they were unable to kill their natural more agile prey, or because they had become accustomed to feeding on human flesh on battlefields or in the vicinity of gallows with rotting corpses. William the Conqueror left the dead English on the battlefield to be eaten by 'worms, wolves, birds, and dogs', and Giraldus refers to wolves scavenging on dead bodies near Holywell after Henry II's punitive expedition into Wales in 1165. It is therefore significant that in Sutherland – by tradition at least – the digging up of graves by wolves was so widespread that the inhabitants of Ederachillis were eventually forced to bury their dead on the island of Handa:

On Ederachillis' shore
  The grey wolf lies in wait –
Woe to the broken door,
  Woe to the loosened gate,
And the groping wretch whom sleety fogs
  On the trackless moor belate.

The lean and hungry wolf,
  With his fangs so sharp and white,
His starveling body pinched
  By the frost of a northern night,
And his pitiless eyes that scare the dark
  With their green and threatening light.

He climbeth the guarding dyke,
  He leapeth the hurdle bars,
He steals the sheep from the pen,
  And the fish from the boat-house spars,
And he digs the dead from out the sod,
  And gnaws them under the stars.

Thus every grave we dug
  The hungry wolf uptore,
And every morn the sod
  Was strewn with bones and gore;
Our mother-earth had denied us rest
  On Ederachillis' shore.

The Book of Highland Minstrelsy, 1846

This practice of burial on small islands was also adopted on Tanera off Wester Ross and on Inishail in Loch Awe, while in Atholl coffins were constructed of five flagstones. It is a curious fact that though wolves are normally averse to eating any kind of carrion, this habit of exhuming corpses has also been reported from North America.

Within the limited bounds of the British Isles men and wolves could not live together indefinitely, whether or not the aristocracy wished to hunt them. South of the Highlands the main factor in their extermination was ever-increasing suppression by the flock-masters – notably those employed by the Cistercians. There is no mention of wolf-hunting on Exmoor after the reign of King John, and though the wolf is referred to as a beast of the Chase in the *Boke of St Albans*, which was published in 1486, this may be hearsay for it is not known when this product of many hands was actually written, though some rhymes on hunting, possibly compiled from existing manuscripts, are traditionally ascribed to Dame Juliana Barnes or Berners, who probably lived early in the fifteenth century, when wolves were still numerous in England. It seems probable that they were finally exterminated in England and Wales between 1485 and 1509, though some may have survived to a later date in the forests of Lancashire and on the Yorkshire wolds. In Ireland, however, the ravages of the wolves – 'bigger of bone and limme than a colt' – became so intolerable after the Catholic rising of 1641, perhaps because of the numbers of unburied corpses, that special wolf hunters were appointed, and eleven years later a law was passed by Cromwell prohibiting the export of 'wolf-dogs'. These magnificent hounds might stand 38 inches at the shoulder and weigh considerably more than 120 pounds. Seven of them had been exhibited in the Imperial Circus in 391 when the Consul, Quintus Aurelius Symmachus, was short of spectacular animals for the Games: 'When the Romans saw them play, they thought them so wonderful violent, as that they must needs have been *Ferreis caveis advecti,* brought up in Iron Dens.' They were almost identical with the now extinct breed of Welsh wolf-dog and in Norman times were the progenitors of the Scottish deer-hound. They probably originated in central Europe, for the Celtic tribes that invaded northern Greece in 273 BC were accompanied by a wolf-hound dog-of-war, derived from a greyhound/saluki type of hound. The Celts called the latter *miol-chù*, which suggests that they may have been used for hunting elk, and the Irish employed them not only against wolves but also against their adversaries in battle. Wolf-spearing was still a popular sport in Ireland in the early years of the eighteenth century, despite the fact that Irish forests had been almost destroyed by 1700, and there is good evidence that the last wolf in Ireland was killed by a pack of wolf-hounds about 1786 in the Mount Leinster district of County Carlow.

We have seen that deforestation in Scotland had begun at a very early date, and already by the twelfth century, when the monks of Melrose Abbey were trapping wolves, a conservation Act, the *Leges Forestarum*, had prohibited the taking of fire or domestic animals into the woods or the felling of oaks; but immense tracts of forest were destroyed from the thirteenth to the fifteenth centuries, by which time wolves may have been exterminated in the Lowlands. In the Highlands the forests were burnt intermittently during the incessant clan feuds, or to clear additional land for the clansmen's very large numbers of small black cattle and considerable flocks of sheep and goats, or to smoke out robbers and the wolves themselves. Burning, however, did not necessarily prevent regeneration of the forests, since this could result in more rapid regrowth. Early in the sixteenth century there was large-scale felling of oak woods, of which the Forest of Caledon contained extensive stands, to meet the demands of shipbuilding; and the Forest was further exploited during the following century to provide charcoal for glass-making and iron-ore smelting in a hundred bloomeries, since the latter had been banned in England by Elizabeth and it was more practicable to transport the ore to accessible forests than to ship timber to smelting works. So widespread was the overall destruction of Highland forests, particularly those of Rannoch, Blair Atholl and Lochaber, that the main forest cover had probably been destroyed by the middle of the seventeenth century, for a map of Aberdeenshire in 1654 shows woodland similar in extent to that of today. Nevertheless, the wolf population in the Highlands was at a peak during the second half of the sixteenth century, with cattle losses from 'very fierce' wolves so severe in Sutherland that in 1577 James VI made a compulsory order that wolf hunts should take place there three times a year; but before the end of the next century they had been virtually exterminated.

Officially, the last Scottish wolf was killed in Killiecrankie (Perthshire) in 1680, but a few are reputed to have survived in Sutherland until the closing years of the century, and undoubtedly did so until a much later date in such wildernesses as the high 'mosses' of the Monadhliath and the Cairngorms. Even today the Monadhliath are as wild and untrodden a waste as may be found in all the Highlands: four hundred square miles of rolling mosses and deep glens, inhabited only by herds of red deer and flocks of feral goats, and by such typical mountain birds as eagles, ravens, golden plover and dotterel. And it was in the region of the upper waters of the Findhorn in the northen Monadhliath that traditionally the last wolf in Scotland was killed in 1743 by the six-foot seven-inches deer-stalker, MacQueen of Poll a'chrocain – as recounted by the brothers John Sobieski and Charles Edward Stuart, who, if not of the noble Highland lineage to which they laid claim, were most observant naturalists and extraordinarily erudite and widely read in the old Gaelic literature. According to their *Lays of the Deer Forest*, it was on a winter's day that MacQueen received a message from the Laird of MacIntosh to attend a *tainchel* for a large black wolf, which the previous day had killed two children crossing the hills with their mother:

> In the morning the Tainchel had long assembled, and MacIntosh waited with impatience, but MacQueen did not arrive; his dogs and himself were, however, auxiliaries too important to be left behind, and they continued to wait until the best of a hunter's morning was

gone, when at last he appeared, and the MacIntosh received him with an irritable expression of disappointment.

Ciod e a' chabhag? – 'What was the hurry? – said Poll a'chrocain.

MacIntosh gave an indignant retort, and all present made some impatient reply.

MacQueen lifted his plaid – and drew the black bloody head of the wolf from under his arms – *Sine e dhùibh*! – 'There it is for you!' – said he, and tossed it on the grass in the midst of the surprised circle.

MacIntosh expressed great joy and admiration, and gave him the land called Sean-achan for meat to his dogs.

Poll a'chrocain's descendants still live in the farm at Sean-achan.

The history of the wolf in western Europe has been similar to that in Britain, except that in a more extensive habitat a very few have been able to hold out until the present day. But for how much longer? They were numerous throughout Europe until early in the nineteenth century, and upwards of two thousand were killed in France as late as 1883. Individuals still appear in central France from time to time, having presumably crossed over the mountains from Spain, though none now inhabit the Pyrenees. In Italy their numbers have been reduced to about a hundred running in small packs in the Apennines where, instead of killing sheep in the absence of natural prey, they subsist mainly by scavenging on the quantities of rubbish dumped on the outskirts of every town in the area, though in the winter they regularly visit the villages and prey on the dogs. In Scandinavia, hunters using snow-scooters and helicopters had totally exterminated the Swedish stock of fewer than forty by 1975, and the migrations of wolves from Russia into north Finland have been greatly exaggerated in the press, for during their 'invasion' in the winter of 1975-6 only five were in fact actually killed in Finland.

6 Mass Extermination by the Game Preservers

After the climate in Britain had settled into its present pattern some 2,500 years ago deforestation and to a lesser degree hunting were initially the main factors inimical to wildlife. Later, sheep-farming was to be no less harmful, and subsequently both mammals and birds were profoundly affected by two new developments.

As one wades through volume after volume of the indefatigable John Leland's commendable but intolerably tedious account of his peregrinations the length and breadth of England and Wales in the late 1530s, his repeated allusions to 'corn, grass, and wood' in one locality after another make it clear that farming changes were also altering the wildlife habitat. However, the major impact of this agricultural revolution would not be felt until the series of Enclosure Acts between 1750 and 1845, when three or four million acres of the old open-field cultivation, together with two million acres of heath and wasteland, were transformed into a chequer-board of small square fields divided up by thousands of miles of hedges, studded with oak and elm trees. But again, although it is generally stated that there were virtually no hedges in England prior to the Enclosures this does not accord with William Harrison's reference to 'infinite numbers of hedgerows' in his *Description of Britaine and England*, the three books of which were pre-fixed to Holinshed's *Chronicles*, printed in 1577 and expanded ten years later. Enclosure did not necessarily imply conversion to permanent pasture, for on the chalk and limestone uplands corn was grown on the enclosed lands. In 1808, for example, Colonel Thomas Thornton – whom we shall meet again – was obliged to move from Thornville Royal in the Yorkshire wolds to Wiltshire because the introduction of corn was spoiling his falconry, though he also flew his falcons at kites over the heaths and warrens of Norfolk and Suffolk.

Much more harmful than the Enclosures was the introduction of firearms, for in 1635 the crossbow began to be superseded by the flintlock, though the latter was not finally perfected until early in the nineteenth century, and the crossbow continued in use by fowlers until the latter half of the eighteenth century. In 1835 the flintlock was in its turn superseded by the breech-loader, of which a primitive form had actually been invented more than three hundred years earlier. The ease with which the breech-loader could be handled and the speed with which it could be reloaded, together with the subsequent refinement of watertight copper percussion-caps, enabled the sportsman to indulge in mass slaughter. Game could now be driven to the gun instead of being walked up; and this innovation held the additional advantage for the sportsman that he had no longer to get out of bed at two o'clock in the morning in order to be on the hill by dawn and then walk and shoot till dusk. Thus, by the latter half of the nineteenth century the traditional rough shooting over pointers working the waste land, thick old hedges, undrained ponds and patches of rushes for snipe and duck was going out of fashion, to be replaced by the *Battue*, in which game or hand-reared pheasants were driven by small armies of beaters towards the guns; and war was declared between game preservers and Masters of Foxhounds.

This revolution in shooting technique stimulated the growth of sporting estates, with the result that by the middle of the nineteenth century, and from then on until the Second World War, the survival or otherwise of Britain's fauna was determined predominantly by the landed proprietors and their gamekeepers. Britain became the most intensively keepered country in the world. Indeed H. L. Edlin has asserted in *The Changing Wild Life of Britain* that the fauna described by contemporary naturalists was not truly representative, but the fauna that the landowners permitted to exist. Deer, grouse, hares, pheasants, partridges, wildfowl, salmon and trout were to be preserved for sport, as were lowland foxes: the rest were vermin to be destroyed in the interests of game or to provide a day's rough shooting. Osgood MacKenzie of Inverewe in Wester Ross was, for example, an enlightened landowner, so far as his tenantry and property were concerned; yet he was an inveterate killer of every kind of wildlife from sea-birds to deer, and characteristically naïve in his assessment of the effects of his shooting and game preserving. I quote from his *One Hundred Years in the Highlands*, which spanned his own lifetime from 1842 to 1922 and also that of his uncle's diary from 1803: 'My mother used to have an average of forty or fifty skins of martens brought to her by the keepers every year.' And again:

> We still have in use a big rug of badgers' skins . . . All caught in this place, though, as in the case of eagles, we had no wish to exterminate them like wild cats and foxes; in fact we should have liked to preserve them, but they would not keep out of the vermins' traps, and so they soon became extinct.

Yet the final result was that blackgame, for example, had vanished from his extensive shootings by about 1915: 'What a big pile it would make if all the blackgame I shot between 1855 and 1900 were gathered in one heap. Now alas! there are none, and why, who can tell.'

7 A Nucleus of the Climbers Survive

> And no one should call or say 'wood cat', 'pole cat', or 'squirrel', but call them grey climber, black climber, red climber . . . And when a climber is chased it cannot flee far from the hounds but takes to a tree to defend itself. And there it is tired out and barked at.

Let us consider how our surviving mammals escaped the general holocaust. Three predators – wild cat, pine marten and polecat – might well have suffered the same fate as bears and wolves, but for the fact that they were small and partly nocturnal, while the two world wars allowed them some respite from persecution; the extensive plantings by the Forestry Commission since the First World War, coupled with the decline of the great sporting estates since the Second World War, have also given them a boost. It is difficult for us to credit how numerous these 'vermin' were in Britain in the days of our grandfathers and great-grandfathers. During the brief period from 1837-40, for example, 198 wild cats, 246 martens and 106 polecats were trapped on a single estate in Glen Garry, Inverness-shire – assuming that the keeper did not exaggerate his bounty claim.

Wild Cats

It was perhaps fortunate for the wild cat that the lynx, almost twice its size, became extinct in Britain at such an early date, for on the Continent lynxes are known to prey on cats, despite the fact that the latter are extremely aggressive animals, with the unusual reputation of attacking man without provocation. Moreover, both would have competed for much the same game; though no doubt their hunting territories did not overlap extensively, for predators must necessarily always be much less numerous than their prey and therefore dispersed over wide areas. Why the lynxes should have become extinct in Britain, while the wild cats were able to survive in this, the northern limit of their range – they have never inhabited Scandinavia or Finland – must remain a problem, for we know so little about the life history of either. However, with the extinction of the lynxes, the wild cats were left with a vacant predatorial niche in Britain, particularly that of dense forest with access to moors and hills, where their main prey were rabbits and mountain hares, supplemented by occasional grouse, fish and large insects. In Europe, where their stronghold now lies in the Balkans, since they are probably extinct in both the Vosges and the Pyrenees, a male cat is reputed to hold a territory of about 175 acres, which it defends against other males, though roaming far outside this home range when in search of a mate. In Britain the cats were most numerous in the forests, though Dent has pointed out that place-names indicate that they were also unusually common on coastal cliffs in Yorkshire, where no doubt they fed well on rabbits in winter and on the eggs and young of nesting sea-birds in the summer, and scavenged the tideline for dead fish. By contrast, there are no coastal place-names attributable to wolves, which, in the Wolds, preferred 'high ground of an open nature, so long as it offered gullies and ravines for their dens.'

There are no historical references to wild cats in Ireland, while in England and, surprisingly, Wales, their extermination began at a very early date. There is, for example, no certain reference to them on Exmoor after 1283, and they had been virtually exterminated in England by the middle of the nineteenth century, though a very large male, 46 inches long but only 18 pounds in weight, was shot in a Lincolnshire wood in 1883. They were also extinct in the Border country before the 1850s, somewhat earlier than in the south-central Highlands, where their history can be traced back as far as AD 200, when the Highlands were the military centre of two Pictish clans, the Orcs (Boars) and Cats (Cat clan). The latter were the ancestors of Gillichattan Mór and Muriach, the Prior of Kingussie, from whom the MacPhersons are descended and whose Chief's personal crest portrays a wild cat, full face and defiant, with claws 'ungloved', together with the motto: 'Touch not the Cat but a Glove.'

With the decline in the number of gamekeepers since the First World War and the increase in the acreage of state forests – in which wild cats are regarded as beneficial controllers of rodents, whereas on grouse moors they are invariably shot or trapped – their numbers have increased in the Highlands to such an extent that one keeper has recently been credited with having killed a hundred in a single year, and their range has been extended southwards and over the Borders into the vast Kielder forest in Northumberland.

Pine Martens

In his account of Ireland, Giraldus observed that:

> Martins are very plentiful in the woods; in hunting which the day is prolonged through the night by means of fires. For night coming on, a fire is lighted under the tree in which the hunted animal has taken

12. A Pine Marten

refuge from the dogs, and being kept burning all night, the martin eyeing its brightness from the boughs above, without quitting its post, either is so fascinated by it, or, rather, so much afraid of it that when morning comes the hunters find him in the same spot.

Though formerly widely distributed, pine martens were also brought near to extinction in Britain as a result of deforestation and persecution by fur trappers, sportsmen and gamekeepers. In the opinion of that excellent naturalist George Bolam, their destructiveness to game was exaggerated, as was that of polecats to poultry, though the nineteenth-century naturalist Thomas Bell refers to an instance of sixteen turkeys being killed in a single night by a polecat. Writing in the early years of this century, Bolam made the interesting point that the employment of Highlanders as gamekeepers on many Welsh estates resulted in much more ruthless keepering, and that this factor, together with the introduction of the steel trap, was mainly responsible for the decline in the numbers of carnivores in Wales and other parts of Britain. That viable populations of martens have been able to survive to this day in Snowdonia, the Lakes, south-west Ireland and the north-west Highlands must be attributed mainly to their ability to adapt to new habitats, though also to their crepuscular and nocturnal habits and to their agility, since they can climb faster than squirrels and run faster than a roe deer: 'When before hounds on level and snow-clad ground they proceed with a succession of astonishing leaps, often six or seven feet apart.' They may also have been able to move into niches formerly occupied by polecats, for the latter apparently never colonised Ireland and are now probably extinct in the Highlands and also the Lowlands. The pine martens' natural habitat was pine forest – spruce forest in Europe – in which they preyed on squirrels and other rodents and also on birds and their eggs; but during the summer months they moved to more open country, where they obtained up to 90 per cent of their food on the ground, preying mainly on small birds and mammals, but also feeding on carrion, on beetles and other large insects, on salmon and trout up to three or four pounds, and taking large quantities of berries. Thus, when persecution drove them out of the old Highland pine forests, they were able to adapt to an all-the-year-round existence in the rocky cairns of the mainly treeless moors and hills of Wester Ross and north-west Sutherland, hunting over a range many miles in circumference, from sea-level to 3,000 feet. In Wales they were, according to Bolam, almost invariably located in mountainous regions by his time. In the Lake District they no doubt inhabited the woods in the days when a squirrel could travel through the trees without ever descending to the ground from the fell head above Troutbeck to Lake Windermere; but there too, as a result of extensive deforestation, they were obliged to retreat to the crags and rocky 'borrans' of the open fellsides. In the nineteenth century they were described as normally keeping to the screes and fells for the greater part of the year, preying on rabbits, mice and birds: 'Though they usually come down to the woods in the valleys in April and May to have their young ones, selecting some old magpie's nest or squirrel's dray: still they sometimes breed in the rocks, near the tops of the highest hills.'

When hunted in Cumberland with small packs of special mart hounds, though also with foxhounds, the martens usually sought sanctuary in the fell screes. That legendary Cumberland yeoman, John Peel, who ran a pack of foxhounds for the first fifty years of the nineteenth century on an income of less than £400 per annum, also hunted marts and hares with his pack, and Lakeland folk believed that the martens were evicted or actually killed by the increasing numbers of foxes. 'Where Foxes is rank, Marts is scarce.' However, as early as 1759 a Cumberland shoot accounted for fifteen foxes, seven badgers, twelve wild cats, nine martens and many polecats. In Westmorland and Merioneth wire-haired terriers were used for martens, and a contributor to *The Field* in 1901 describes how the most favourable time for tracking them was when the mountains were lightly, but evenly, covered with unfrozen snow:

> The cat-like impression of the Marten's paw is . . . easily recognised. Very often the trail is a long one, for Martens will travel as far as foxes during the night, and they often take a straighter line across the shoulders of mountains . . . The Chase leads on through steep masses of heather, over great boulders, and across boggy places to the summit . . . The rough-coated black and tan Welsh terrier . . . darts into a cavern . . . The Marten swells out its brush, erects the

hairs on its back, and spits and hisses like a cat. Pinning the dog by the nose the plucky beast fights viciously and retreats.

With the change in land use since the last war from sheep-farming and shooting to forestry, martens have begun to increase in numbers and have spread south of the Great Glen; but according to Richard Balharry, who has studied them intensively in the Highlands, at least a hundred are still killed every year in Scotland, mainly in gin-traps set for foxes. Since every account of pine martens in both Britain and Europe emphasises their habit of travelling long distances, and suddenly appearing in localities in which they are believed to have been extinct for many years, they should be able to take advantage of the ever-increasing areas of state forest and extend their range still further.

There is no evidence that the very similar beech or stone martens, with their smaller ears, white throat-patch and less hairy pads, ever inhabited Britain, despite nineteenth-century claims to the contrary, which were perhaps based on the tendency for both Welsh and English pine martens to display more white on the throat than Scottish ones. Although the distribution of the two species overlaps in Europe, the pine martens range further north to the limits of the spruce forests, whereas the beech martens typically inhabit deciduous woodlands as far south as the Mediterranean region. Nevertheless the latter also travel far afield and in the Alps climb 10,000 feet to ridges that have been swept clear of snow by the winds, in order to feed on the tough but nutritious red berries of the strawberry-tree. Though their prey is similar to the pine martens' they are less arboreal, but more strictly nocturnal, and much less shy of man, lying up in hay stacked in granaries and commonly frequenting alpine villages where they catch mice in outhouses and stables.

Polecats

Once the pine forests had been decimated, the pine marten or sweet mart can never have been as widely distributed as the polecat or foul-smelling foumart – not that dogs find the scent of the former less attractive than that of the latter. The natural habitat of polecats included not only glades and ravines in deciduous woods but also the bushy banks of rivers, lakes and marshes where snakes, fish, eels and amphibians could be caught; and Thomas Bell described finding five young polecats in a nest of dry withered grass, which had been provisioned with forty large frogs and two toads, all of which were alive but paralysed by being bitten through the brain – a practice subsequently confirmed by a French naturalist. However, according to William Condry, writing in *Oryx*, polecats do not, as has been stated, migrate in large numbers in the spring to the great Welsh peatbog of Tregaron in order to prey on the spawning frogs, because this bog, in addition to being too wet to be habitable and offering few holes in which to lie up, is not in fact a metropolis of spawning frogs. The polecats' main stronghold in Britain within living memory has been the rough grazings, honeycombed with rabbit warrens, of the semi-upland farms of mid-Wales, where more than five hundred – though only a dozen martens – were killed during the years 1926-31. In the Lake District they were usually to be found in bog land or heather, with their lairs in stone heaps, drains or old barns, and 173 – though only four pine martens – were killed in this type of open country around Kendal in 1794. Until the middle of the nineteenth century they were hunted from early in February until the end of April with nondescript packs of dogs on the Welsh hills and Lakeland fells – though otter hounds were also used on the fells and in the Border country and Scottish Lowlands – and since the hobs or males were roaming long distances in search of mates at that season, a hunt might cover twenty miles.

Initially forest clearance in Britain provided polecats with an additional, farmland, habitat in which voles, mice and birds could be caught at dusk or after dark and stored in their burrows for the young to feed on even before their eyes were open. In Europe, where they have greatly extended their range during the past hundred years in Finland and to a lesser degree in Sweden, in country outside the coniferous forests, they are still neighbours of man during the winter, holing up in village buildings. But in Britain, this close contact with man and his small livestock was to prove disastrous, since they were easy to trap: 'He had a polecat in his hedge that had killed his capons, and he would fain revenge himself, if he might, on vermin that destroyed him by night,' wrote Chaucer; and such indiscriminate killers could not be

13. Polecats Greeting at the Mouth of their Den

tolerated in rabbit warrens which, during the Middle Ages, provided essential supplies of fresh meat. Large numbers were caught in rabbit snares and others were trapped for their fur. In 1510 there was a lawsuit at Colchester concerning three hundred polecat pelts, and six hundred pelts were on sale in the Dumfries fur market in 1831 – but none thirty years later. They were still widely distributed, though much less common, in the nineteenth century, and were to be found near London as late as 1860. However, latter-day records in southern England are open to doubt, for the dark form of domesticated ferret, which closely resembles the wild polecat, was being kept in England as long ago as 1272, when rabbits were being caught with ferrets at Waleton. Since that time there has been constant interbreeding between ferrets and polecats, with the result that possibly very few pure-bred polecats now exist. By the present century the latter had become very rare in the Lakes, though during recent years they have increased rapidly in their Welsh stronghold and have colonised most of the adjacent English counties.

Squirrels

It was not their natural predators, the pine martens, that almost exterminated the red squirrels in the Highlands during the eighteenth and early nineteenth centuries, but a combination of three factors – deforestation, diseases such as cocidiosis, to which squirrels are vulnerable, and a series of severe winters. The latter may possibly have coincided with cyclical failures in the crop of pine seed, since in the *taiga* such failures have resulted in a reduction of the squirrel population to 1/450th of its former strength. An epidemic also resulted in a marked decline in the numbers of red squirrels in England during the first quarter of this century – typically after their population had remained at a peak for ten or twenty years; and no doubt one or more of these factors was responsible for their extinction in Ireland before the end of the seventeenth century. In the Highlands, however, where they were supposed to have become extinct by 1840, a small stock in fact survived in the Rothiemurchus remnant of the Forest of Caledon; and re-afforestation, beginning with the developing plantations around the lairds' estates in the late eighteenth century, enabled this stock, augmented by numerous introductions from England and Wales, and also from Scandinavia, to recolonise the Highlands and also southern Scotland and northern England, despite the shooting of tens of thousands by keepers and foresters. Ireland has also been recolonised, but red squirrels are much less numerous today in England and Wales than in the nineteenth century, though still widespread.

It seems probable that there have been two races of red squirrels in Britain for several thousand years: one in the Highlands and the other in England, separated by a squirrel-less area north and south of the Borders, with the Highland stock living mainly in the pine forests and the English in mixed woods, as is the case in Denmark, where red

14. A Red Squirrel

squirrels are believed to have lived continuously in the deciduous forests for the past two or three thousand years. In Europe they are widely distributed from the northern edge of tree growth to the Mediterranean, but in Scandinavia and the *taiga* inhabit the coniferous forests of spruce, pine and larch. In England, too, their habitat must normally include a certain proportion of mature conifers that will provide seed for food and also 'nesting' trees – preferably Scots pine more than fifteen years old and sufficiently developed to hold the football-sized, woven mass of twigs, grass, moss and shredded bark (often of honeysuckle) of which the dreys are constructed. Some of the latter, lined with similar materials and perhaps sheep's wool,

15. A Grey Squirrel

will serve as nests for the young for a couple of months after birth: others as temporary shelters in the winter, for squirrels do not hibernate. In a mild winter, indeed, the period from autumn to New Year is one of maximum activity. They may be inactive for short periods during spells of continuous gales or heavy snow, because of the difficulty they experience in moving around; but they cannot survive for longer than a few days without food. In January 1945 they were active in Switzerland in temperatures of 5°F, with snow lying twenty inches deep; while in 1947, when there was unbroken frost for 56 consecutive days in the Grampians, they were abroad in temperatures as low as minus 10°F and minus 15°F.

Their very wide range of seasonal foods includes, in the spring, the buds and shoots of young conifers, bulbs, roots and some insects, and later the seed of pine cones; while from April to June when sap, with its high sugar content, is flowing up young conifers, and also when it recedes in July, the squirrels gnaw off the bark in order to tap the sap in the cambium layer between the bark and the newest wood, and also chew the cambium itself. This barking is liable to increase in dry weather, when drinking water is in short supply, and results in young trees being killed if a ring of bark is stripped off near the base. The most favoured trees for this purpose are Scots pine 20 to 40 feet high and from fifteen to forty years old, though larch and spruce are also tapped, whereas grey squirrels bark deciduous trees from eight to forty years old. In summer the diet of the reds is larvae, various fungi (including the most deadly poisonous), and some birds' eggs and nestlings; while during the late summer and autumn, when there is a super-abundance of such foods as acorns, sweet chestnuts, beechmast, cone and plant seed, hazel-nuts, hips and haws, agarics and truffles, they are feverishly active in collecting, burying and storing these. But European squirrels do not normally amass large hoards in the manner of American pine and red squirrels. They either bury their small hoards of nuts, acorns or beechmast, or more usually cache them in old dreys. These hoards often remain untouched throughout the winter, when the squirrels obtain the bulk of their food on the forest floor, for though essentially arboreal, they frequently descend to ground level to forage, and also to drink in hot weather and when migrating from one stand of conifers to another. Nevertheless, although the various locations of buried hoards appear to be forgotten by their owners, they probably serve a purpose, because during their winter excursions the squirrels rediscover their hoards, or chance upon those of other squirrels, and are apparently able to scent these under several inches of snow. A proportion of those fruits that are never found germinate and grow into trees, though probably not of the kind intended by the forester!

As it happened, the decline of the red squirrel stock in England coincided with the main shipments of grey squirrels from North America, since there were more than thirty of these between 1876 and 1929. There must, however, have been earlier introductions, for there are records of what were apparently grey squirrels in east Kent in the eighteenth century and in Montgomery and Denbighshire between 1828 and 1850. A letter to the editor of the *Cambrian Quarterly Magazine* in 1830, for example, states that:

> In some retired glades of Montgomeryshire and Denbighshire . . . a grey squirrel lives and breeds. The specimens I have seen were as large as a . . . three-quarters grown rabbit; the head roundish, the eyes very prominent, the ears shorter than the common red squirrel's and not the slightest appearance of tufts upon them; the body and legs of a fine grey colour, the latter short and muscular and furnished with strong claws; there is a variegation of red along the sides of the ribs . . . the tail is covered with hair rather longer than in the common sort, and a mixture of grey and black . . . They are extremely shy on the approach of man . . . the young are usually produced from the latter half of April to the end of May.

Since the major introductions of grey squirrels occurred when the decline in the numbers of red had left vacant several suitable habitats, especially oakwoods, in the open deciduous woods and parklands of southern England, the grey were able to establish themselves firmly in these and discourage any attempts by the reds to recolonise them when their numbers increased again; and had it not been for this fortuitous synchronisation the grey might not have become a permanent member of the British fauna. But there is no definitive evidence that the grey contributed to the decline of the red or that they subsequently drove them out of their existing strongholds; for while it is true that the recovery of the red has been slow or nil in areas occupied by the grey for ten or fifteen years, this has also been the case in areas where there are no grey. In some localities, for example, both species have coexisted for a number of years in apparent amity before the red have eventually disappeared, while on several occasions the two have been reported feeding in close proximity without friction, especially in Ireland where the red are now numerous and to which the grey were introduced in 1911. However, since 1959 there have been significant replacements of red by grey in some areas. One explanation for these could be that since the grey is much the bolder of the two it can tolerate the ever-increasing human invasion of deciduous woods, whereas the shyer red retreats to the less popular pine woods. Alternatively, while the latter can subsist throughout the year on the foods provided by a coniferous wood, it may be hard-pressed to find sufficient at midwinter, whereas the grey, being omnivorous and eating virtually anything edible, and inhabiting mainly mixed deciduous woods, can choose from a variety of nuts and seeds should one or more types of tree fail to fruit. It can indeed discriminate between the acorns of different kinds of oaks, possibly favouring those with a higher content of sugar and less of tannin.

In the mixed woods of England the grey squirrels have thrived. By the 1920s, thirty years after the first introduction to Woburn Park, they had colonised 1,350 square miles of the surrounding country, by 1937 more than 9,600 square miles and by 1960 38,600 square miles; and they continue to spread slowly, with individuals pressing forward through at present unoccupied regions into Northumberland and even Inverness-shire, though no permanent colonies have been established in the Highlands north of Perthshire.

8 The Most Marvellous Beast in the World

The most ancient races of hares in Britain, with Pleistocene ancestry, are the blue mountain hares of Scotland – which are identical with the arctic hares of northern Europe and the Alps – and the Irish hares, which much resemble them. The latter, however, tend to be somewhat larger and rarely moult into the full winter-white pelage of the mountain hares, whose fine-spun fringe of long silky hair on the belly brushes the snow as they skitter over the frozen moors. No doubt they were one and the same before Ireland was cut off from the mainland of Britain; and the blue hares must once have inhabited the uplands between North Wales and the Scottish Lowlands – to which they were re-introduced with varying success during the nineteenth century – until the ice-sheet receded far enough north for them to colonise the Highlands. In Ireland hares have been abundant for centuries. It will be recalled that an old Irish tract referred to 'little hares', and Giraldus observed that in Ireland:

> There are a great number of hares, but they are a small breed, much resembling rabbits both in size and the softness of their fur . . . When found by the dogs, they keep to cover like foxes, running in the woods instead of in the open country, and never taking to the plains and beaten paths, unless they are driven to it. This difference in their habits is, I think, caused by the rankness of the herbage in the plains, checking their speed.

Brown hares, being post-glacial arrivals in Britain, were never indigenous in Ireland, though they have since been introduced, as Irish hares have been imported to England for coursing. Although the brown hares were plentiful in England at the time of the Roman invasion, the Britons, according to Caesar, 'account it wrong to eat of hare, fowl, and goose; but these they keep for pastime or for pleasure'; but by the time of *The Nine Huntings* the four chief 'venison' were stag, hare, wild boar and bear. It was the Normans who initiated the hunting of the hare, and also coursing with greyhounds, in Britain. William Twici or Twyti or William the Twin, etc., etc., grand huntsman to Edward II (1307-27) and author of the first hunting treatise by an Englishman – though it was printed as *Le Art de Venerie* – described the hare or Puss as 'the most merveylous best in the world'; while Gaston de Foix wrote that: 'It is fair thing to slay her with strength of hounds, for she runneth strong and cunningly. A hare shall last well four miles or less, if she be an old male hare.' Hares were believed to be hermaphrodite.

By Tudor times the hare was the hunter's main quarry, and there was not much that the early hunters did not know about the field habits of hares, as the following extract from *The Master of Game* indicates:

> When a hare ariseth out of her form to go to her pasture or return again to her seat, she commonly goes by one way, and as she goes she will not suffer any twig or grass to touch her, for she will sooner break it with her teeth and make her way. Sometimes she sitteth a mile or more from her pasturing, and sometimes near her pasture . . . And whether she go to sit near or far from her pasture she goes gynously and wilily that there is no man in this world that would say that any hound could unravel that which she has done, or that could find her. For she will go a bow shot or more by one way, and ruse again by another, and then she shall take her way by another side, and the same she shall do ten, twelve, or twenty times, from thence she will come in to some hedge or strength, and shall make semblance to abide there, and then will make cross roads ten or twelve times, and will make her ruses, and thence she will take some false path, and shall go thence a great way, and such semblance she will make many times before she goeth to her seat.
>
> The hare that runneth with right standing ears is but little afraid, and is strong, and yet when she holdeth one ear upright and the other laid low on her ryge, she feareth but little the hounds. An hare that crumps her tail upon her rump when she starteth out of her form as a cony it is a token that she is strong and well running.

Throughout the sixteenth and seventeenth centuries, and for much of the eighteenth, hares provided the squires and farmers with their principal sport and the supreme test of hunting skill: 'The *Hare* maketh the best Diversion and sheweth the most Cunning in Hunting.' During his energetic Rural Rides between 1821 and 1830 William Cobbett (himself the son of a farm labourer) found time for many days' coursing with greyhounds on the Wiltshire downs:

> miles and miles square without a tree, or hedge, or bush. It is a country of greensward. This is the most famous place in all England for *coursing* . . . There were forty brace of greyhounds taken out into the field on one of the days . . . The ground is the finest in the

16. Common Hares Chasing Each Other

see over

world; from two to three miles for the hare to run to cover, and not a stone nor a bush nor a hillock.

Cobbett brought down a cartful of hares from Berkshire to turn out on one of his farms; and when their numbers were at a peak at the end of the nineteenth century they were widely distributed over arable land and pasture, woodlands, heaths and moors, being particularly numerous in East Anglia, where on 19 December 1877 eleven guns shot 1,212. In hilly districts of England and Wales they may range as high as 2,000 feet, but in many parts of Scotland tend to be replaced by the blue hares above 1,000 feet.

Predominantly a solitary animal, the brown hare lies out in the open or in a 'form' in a tuft or grass, selected to give a good field of view, shelter from the prevailing wind, and as much sun as possible in the winter; and even on the bitterest winter night may lie out on the bare fallow. Even the leverets – fully furred and with eyes and ears open, in contrast to young rabbits, naked, blind and deaf in their burrow nests – are born in the open and, reputedly, immediately carried by the doe to separate forms and suckled independently for probably no longer than three or four weeks. Then they too go their own ways. They will be sexually mature when eight or twelve months old, if they survive; for in their exposed habitat they are particularly defenceless when young against such predators as foxes, stoats, polecats and feral cats, whereas when adult their fleetness of foot, ability to turn in their own length, and leap ditches and obstacles of Grand National calibre must render them almost immune. Moreover, their large eyes, placed at the side of the head, give them wide-angle vision, which they improve upon by sitting up on their hind legs from time to time. Like deer, however, they have difficulty in detecting stationary objects, and one will lope leisurely up a path to within thirty feet of such a large figure as a man standing motionless. This limitation must render them vulnerable to stalking predators such as foxes.

Brown hares are usually gregarious only during the mating season. This, though traditionally falling in March, actually extends from December into spring and early summer. Then, on odd days half a dozen or more individuals will collect together in a field, perhaps to indulge in no more aggressive antics than some tentative 'boxing' or skipping, but on other occasions to fight fiercely: bucks with bucks, and bucks with does that are not ready to mate. Rearing up on their hind legs, they strike rapidly and vigorously with forefeet, or leap into the air and strike at each other's bellies with their hind feet. We can surmise that these regular trysting places serve the purpose of bringing together for mating the widely scattered population of hares. But though not normally gregarious, there are unexplained occasions when they associate in very much larger numbers. Cobbett, for instance, once saw 'an acre of hares' near Amesbury: 'Mr Beech . . . took us into a wheat stubble . . . his son took a gallop round, cracking his whip . . .

The hares . . . started all over the field, ran into a *flock* like sheep; and we all agreed that the flock did cover *an acre of ground*.' More recently hares have formed the habit of concentrating in scores or hundreds on airfields in various parts of Britain and on the Continent: not apparently to graze on the expanses of greensward, but in response to some peculiar attraction – possibly the noise or vibrations of aircraft, since they are also excited by thunder. Irish hares have long been known to gather in herds of three or four hundred, though there do not appear to be any accounts of what takes place at these gatherings; but though a Scottish moor may be 'alive' with blue hares, chasing each other in twos or threes, this seems to be more a matter of weight of numbers than of assembly for a purpose. On a November day in Perthshire, for example, 1,289 blue hares were shot by six guns.

During the course of this century there has been some reduction in the population of brown hares and some contraction in their distribution in Britain, due partly perhaps to the number of leverets killed by mowing and reaping machines; but though many adults and young may die of starvation in a hard winter, or from food poisoning through eating the bark of broom, which contains the toxic alkaloids cystisine and sparteine, this mortality cannot account for the erratic fluctuations in their numbers. They are not afflicted with the unfortunate rabbit's loathsome plagues, and are virtually immune from myxomatosis, for the only known instance of infection in Britain occurred in a single locality in Ireland, though there have been some other instances in France and Germany. No doubt the hare population is subject to cycles of peaks and lows controlled by a combination of obscure factors.

◄7. A Blue Hare

9 In Setts, Holts and Earths They Also Survive

Should one hear a badger call
And then an ullot cry,
Make thy peace with God, good soul,
For shortly thou shalt die.

Badgers

The brock, grey, pate or bawson until the mid-eighteenth century has been a very stubborn inhabitant of Britain, though not of any of the offshore islands except Anglesey and the Isle of Wight. Carew, writing in 1600 of the badgers' paths among the cromlechs and stone circles on the Cornish moors, and of their setts – a mile or so apart – in the brakes and cairns and in the cliffs around Land's End, referred to these as the badgers' ancient inheritance. Long and relentless persecution has failed to eradicate them, though one chronicler at the end of the sixteenth century observed that they would have been exterminated before his time had it not been for the sanctuary of deer parks; and at intervals they have been almost wiped out locally as, for example, in the Lake District in the eighteenth century, after the inhabitants had been possessed by some corporate lunacy the previous century to begin a general massacre of wildlife in the dales and on the fells.

For the past fifty or sixty years, however, the badgers have been recolonising the Lakes, and are now climbing back into the fell strongholds of their ancestors, though there, as elsewhere in Britain, their persecution continues because they offer sport in baiting; because their setts make good refuges for hunted foxes; because gamekeepers believe that badgers take sitting pheasants and partridges and their eggs, of which there is very little confirmation; and because farmers believe mistakenly that they are habitual killers of poultry and lambs, whereas poultry-killing is rare and lamb-killing totally without reputable evidence: a vixen living in a badger's sett being the usual culprit. On the contrary, badgers are good friends to both farmers and game-

18. A Badger Leaving its Sett

keepers, since they consume large numbers of injurious insects and also kill rats, mice, voles and rabbits. Indeed young rabbits, which a badger locates by scenting out the position of a nest and then digging vertically down to it, constitute the main food when available, though earthworms and acorns are also important items in their diet.

That badgers have been able to survive centuries of persecution must be attributed partly to their nocturnal habits and partly to the impregnability of the older setts, despite the obvious presence of these. Many are hundreds of years old and of enormous extent – particularly in the West Country – and in his *British Wild Animals*, Mortimer Batten described one, outwardly small and with only a single entrance at the base of a low cliff near Hutton-le-Hole in the Yorkshire limestone country, from which terriers would emerge in the next dale nearly a mile distant. The sleeping chamber may be sixty yards in from the nearest exit, and a sett's ramifications, including three storeys of tunnels, may cover an acre of woodland and have more than fifty entrances, though only a few of these will be in use at one time. A badger's ideal environment is provided by deciduous woodland with its ample ground cover:

> Of foxes we have some, but no real store, and also badgers in our sandy and light grounds, where woods, furze, broom and plenty of shrubs are to shrowd them in, when they be from their burrows, and thereunto warrens of conies at hand to feed upon at will

wrote William Harrison; but abandoned mine shafts have been used for setts in Cornwall, and the badger is one animal that has not benefited from the Forestry Commission's conifer plantings, because these lack ground cover. A hilly terrain is preferred both in Britain and on the Continent – where badgers are to be found almost everywhere except in the northern regions of Scandinavia and in Russia – and the setts are often near water and may even be tunnelled into stream banks well above the water-line.

In Britain the numbers of badgers had probably been reduced to an all-time low by 1914, before some respite from persecution during the two wars allowed them to increase and extend their range again. Since 1945, however, illegal gassing by farmers and keepers, industrial and urban expansion, the new hazards of motorways and electrified railways, and most recently the infection of some badgers by bovine tuberculosis in a limited area of the West Country, have once again endangered the survival of some populations in England, though it is unlikely that they can ever be exterminated in the wilder parts of Britain. In 1976 the Mammal Society estimated that there were then between eighteen and twenty thousand setts in England, including about six thousand in the south-west, together with four to five thousand in Wales and possibly between three to five thousand in Scotland. From these estimates it was reckoned that the winter population of badgers in England, Scotland and Wales might total between 75,000 and 90,000. This would be increased by the birth of cubs during the early months of the year, but since the mortality among the latter is considerable the population would become adjusted once more by late autumn.

Otters

Late in the tenth century Aelfric – the prolific West Saxon writer of saints' lives and homilies – recounted how when St Cuthbert was staying for some days in the Coldingham monastery near St Abb's Head:

> He would go in the night to the sea, and stand in the salt flood to his neck, chanting his prayers. Then on a summer night another monk listened for his going, and with a stealthy stalking his footsteps followed, until they both came to the sea. Then did Cuthbert ... sing his prayers ... and, after, bowed his knees on the sand, stretching the palms of his hands to the heavenly sky. Just then two otters came from the bottom of the sea, and they with their fleece dried his feet ... and, after, with beckonings begged his blessings, lying at his feet on the yellow sand. Then Cuthbert sent back the sea beasts to the water with true blessings, and at morning sought the minster.

But one of the reasons for the scarcity of otters in our overcrowded twentieth-century Britain is their almost pathological sensitivity to disturbance by man and his machines. There are, for instance, reported to be only about thirty left in Norfolk, whose broads and fens with their abundant fish and waterfowl and acres of dense reed-beds and carr covert formerly provided an ideal environment. Their continued survival is indeed at risk in many parts of Britain, and has been for a long time past, for Richard Jefferies, writing in 1887, noted that they were 'sadly scarce' in many counties, though Somerset was an exception. Their precarious status is due mainly to two factors – the drainage and pollution of their habitat, and the firm belief among anglers and river keepers that otters are destructive to trout and salmon. To these factors must be added hunting – an anachronism that dates back at least as far as King John's reign, when the use of a three-pronged spear made the sport slightly more barbarous – though today reputedly only two packs of otter-hounds actually kill any otters they find. A fourth factor is the rather surprising continued demand for pelts, and on some famous salmon rivers in Ireland the stocks of otters have been nearly exterminated, not in order to preserve the fish but by systematic trapping for pelts. So far as their alleged destructiveness to fish is concerned, these actually constitute considerably less than half of the average otter's total food intake, and only 20 per cent of these are salmon and trout: the remainder being coarse fish, including pike up to twenty pounds in weight and especially eels. Moreover, eels are almost invariably preferred to game fish, and although otters will kill and eat almost any prey, including duck and other wildfowl, they are not normally indiscriminate killers, except in the artificial conditions of trout and salmon hatcheries. They have indeed been described as lazy opportunists, preferring the easiest catch – torpid frogs and eels in the winter, spawning fresh-water crayfish in the early summer, and sickly fish or small fishes swimming in compact shoals.

Though otters have always been widely distributed in Britain, and throughout Europe, they are nowhere very numerous, being mainly solitary of habit. Even on the well-stocked fishing waters of large river systems their maximum density is probably no more than one to every five or six miles of river bank or lake shore. This represents the dog-otter's home range, which he patrols at more or less regular intervals, and mainly at night because of widespread persecution, using the same trails year after year; and except during the breeding season otters are constantly on the move within their territories, rarely spending two consecutive nights in the same place. In the wilder terrain of Scotland, however, they often travel ten or fifteen miles overland, particularly when migrating to breeding places at remote hill lochs or in sea caves. It is possible that on salmon and trout streams the wanderings of some otters tend to coincide with the seasonal migrations of the fish, as they follow them up to the spawning redds in the late autumn and go downstream with the younger fish in the spring. In the West Highlands, as in Ireland and Norway, they tend to be marine rather than riverine animals, living on small islands as much as five miles off the mainland and feeding entirely on sea fish and molluscs.

Foxes

Although there is apparently only one cave painting, probably Magdalenian, depicting a fox, remains indicate that it was an ancient inhabitant of Britain; but one suspects that foxes were never very common in these islands until comparatively recently, for heavy forest is not their natural habitat, despite the ease with which they climb trees. They had also to contend with the wolves. However, they were familiar enough to the eighth-century Northumbrian scholars. Bede wrote:

> The nature of foxes accords well with the ways and the words of heretics, for they are exceedingly deceitful creatures who lie hidden in dens and caves, and when they do come out they never run on a straight course but follow devious paths . . .

while Alcuin advised the monks of Wearmouth and Jarrow more practically to: 'Let the boys be present with praises of the heavenly king, and not be digging foxes out of holes or following the fleeting courses of hares.'

With their ability to adapt to a diversity of habitats, whether lowland farms or upland pastures, forestry plantations, moors or mountains, sea cliffs and caves, disused mines and most recently large towns, foxes have been able to colonise all Britain except Orkney and Shetland and the Hebrides other than Skye: 'There's a tod aye blinkin' when the nicht comes down.' No doubt they were treated as vermin from the earliest days. One of the conditions for holding land in the thirteenth century involved the destruction of foxes, wolves, cats and 'other vermin', and fox control had already begun in Scotland at that time. However, early that century Layamon gave a description of fox-hunting (and also of hawking cranes in the Fens), and *The Nine Huntings* subsequently stated that:

> These are the nine huntings every man should know who sounds a horn. And when a huntsman carries a horn is asked concerning these huntings, unless he reply satisfactorily concerning them, he who questions him can, by law, take his horn away. The three first are called common hunts; namely a stag, a swarm of bees, and a salmon: the second is called a hunt with baying, namely, a bear, a climber, and a cock of the wood . . . The third is called a hunt with cries, namely, a fox, a hare, and a roebuck . . . Why is it said that the fox is one of the hunts with cries? Because it defends itself despite the shouting which follows it and the sounding of horns.

But despite the 'sounding of horns' the usual method of hunting foxes in those days, as described by Chaucer and others, was to net the sides of a copse and then use dogs – possibly small beagle-type hounds, which may also have been used for hunting hares – to drive the fox into the net, and then despatch it with sticks. During the sixteenth century foxes were still being destroyed by villagers as vermin at the parish's expense over much of England, though it was William Harrison's opinion that:

> If I may freely say what I think, I suppose that [foxes and badgers] are rather preserved by gentlemen to hunt and have pastime withal at their own pleasures . . . For such is the scarcity of them here in England . . . and so earnestly are the inhabitants bent to root them out, that, except it had been to bear thus with the recreations of their superiors in this behalf it could not otherwise have been chosen but that they should have been utterly destroyed by manie years agone.

According to the memoirs of the Rev. John Russell, even in the early years of the nineteenth century there were districts where the church bell was rung when a fox had been marked to ground, to summon 'every man who possessed a pick-axe, a gun or a terrier to hasten to the spot and lend a hand in destroying the noxious animal'; and not until

9. A Red Fox
see over

the Golden Age of fox-hunting, which lasted from the middle of that century until the First World War, did vulpicide entail such social stigma that a dying Essex farmer could warn his children: 'Better kill a man than a fox.'

The sixteenth-century *The Noble Art of Venerie* had included instructions for hunting the fox above ground, and there is an Elizabethan record of foxes being hunted with greyhounds in Essex, while in Derbyshire Sir Thomas Cockayne was already at that time entering his hound puppies to foxes – 'after which they will not chase hares or rabbits, nor any other chase save a vermin [fox]'. But early packs of hounds normally hunted foxes, hares and deer indiscriminately, and packs maintained exclusively for fox-hunting were virtually unknown until the end of the seventeenth century – when foxes were still apparently not very common – and did not become fashionable for another hundred years. Fox-hunting as a national sport was made possible by the Enclosures, when the large-scale planting of hedges transformed the shires in particular into what has been aptly termed a steeplechaser's Valhalla. The hedges were composed mainly of hawthorn, which had been in use since Saxon times for constructing impenetrable stockades, and whose name was derived from the old English *laga*, an enclosure. The seedling hawthorns, protected by a rail, were allowed to grow high and uncut for twenty years – forming the fox-hunter's 'bullfinches', which could be jumped through but not over – before being plashed and laid. The hedge bottoms served as sanctuaries for woodland plants and as trackways for small rodents, while the loosened soil of the new hedge-banks provided ideal burrowing conditions for rabbits, whose numbers multiplied, since they had also been provided with a bountiful supply of grass on the new permanent pastures.

Here then was a perfect habitat for foxes, which also increased. However, as one consequence of the Enclosures had been the replacement of the natural cover of woods and scrub by grass, the hunt Masters were obliged to plant coverts of gorse and blackthorn in order to hold the foxes in their country. Nevertheless, by the late eighteenth century the demand by the various hunts for foxes far exceeded the native supply, and throughout the nineteenth century, and even early in the twentieth, most Masters of Foxhounds were forced to import foxes from the Continent. These came mainly from France and Holland, with regular shipments in rabbit cargoes from Ostend and in cattle-boats from Rotterdam, though others came from Spain, Austria, Germany, Italy, Sardinia, Scandinavia and even Russia; but they all looked alike in the hunting field, despite the Dutch foxes being described as 'very lengthy, with ears like donkeys, and very thick brushes.' Some foxes were transported to the hunting shires by the new railway system from those parts of Britain, such as East Anglia and Scotland, where there were fewer hunts, and some Masters refrained from killing their foxes, bagging them for another day's hunting. The Continental trade centred on London's Leadenhall Market, where possibly as many as a thousand foxes were dumped every year, and where, according to Raymond Carr's *English Fox Hunting*, Masters had standing orders: one for half a dozen a week, another receiving 75 brace at fifteen shillings a head in a single consignment. Some of these imported foxes – the 'bagmen' – were, like carted stags, released prior to a meet and hunted again and again on as many as 36 occasions, while others were turned down in the coverts and subsequently bred. Thus today probably all British foxes carry some European blood, for even Highland foxes are conspecific with those of Scandinavia, and while the indigenous Lakeland fell foxes were reputedly greyish in colour and larger on average than Lowland foxes, this type had become rare by the 1920s when, as a result of the introduction of the 'red' strain, the local packs were killing five or six times as many foxes annually as in the late nineteenth century.

As a result of this trafficking foxes had become plentiful in most parts of Britain by the early years of the twentieth century. Since there would appear to be no limit to their adaptability, they have now invaded the human environment, taking up permanent residence not only in suburban areas, where cemeteries provide popular sites for breeding earths, but in the heart of metropolises such as London. There they thrive on rats, mice, household scraps and refuse, and have their earths as near to Piccadilly Circus as Hampstead Heath. Catholicism in the matter of food has been a major factor in the foxes' success, and it was no surprise to find that their predation on hares did not increase appreciably after myxomatosis had decimated the rabbits in Britain. It is true that rabbits had probably provided foxes with their staple food for centuries, except during the summer months when, despite the fact that the rabbit population, swelled by the increment of the young, was then at its peak, a variety of other prey was available, but they had always also taken large numbers of such small mammals as rats and woodmice and, in particular, field voles which they captured in their shallow tunnel systems. Thus it has been estimated that whereas prior to myxomatosis rabbits constituted 50 per cent of a fox's food and voles 10 per cent, this ratio was altered after the plague to 10 per cent of rabbits and 40 per cent of voles, supplemented by such unusual items as silage and by any carrion they came across. The extent to which they might feed on carrion was illustrated by an incident in the spring of 1960 when 1,300 foxes died in East Anglia alone after eating pigeons that had been poisoned by toxic seed dressings. One tends to think of seed dressing as an evil associated with modern farming practice, but as long ago as the mid-nineteenth century the Norfolk naturalist Henry Stevenson had expressed his satisfaction that the poisoning of wheat grain in order to kill birds was no longer permitted; adding that yellowhammers, visiting stackyards in winter, had been particularly affected.

That only a very small number of Britain's 55 million inhabitants have ever seen or consciously heard wild foxes, despite their wide distribution and often close proximity, can be attributed to three factors. Firstly, they are mainly nocturnal: almost entirely so in the case of the vixen, when she is not hunting for her cubs. Secondly, they are predominantly solitary of habit, except during the winter clicketting or mating season, though a dozen may collect at the frozen carcase of a deer in a hard Highland winter, while in hunting country they naturally travel much more widely and come into more frequent contact with other foxes. And thirdly, they, like otters, tend to be frequently on the move from one locality to another at intervals of days or weeks, hunting over a radius of several square miles and ringing the changes on earths or temporary burrows. Yet, like hares, they are essentially surface-living animals, with dog-foxes in particular above ground for the greater part of the year, and only occasionally making use of earths. The latter are primarily nurseries for the cubs and burrowing is perhaps an acquired habit, for vixens rarely excavate their own holes, but enlarge existing rabbit burrows. St Leger-Gordon has described how the rabbit, though dispossessed, does not relinquish its burrow:

> It digs a basement . . . and this the fox annexes also in due course. The patient rabbit perseveres. The fox . . . continues to improve upon its tenement, and so with the passage of time have resulted the great main earths . . . Whether a great main earth has actually been developed by fox or badger its history is the same. Once established, it spreads like a subterranean town, or rather perhaps like a block of flats.

Great earths, like badgers' setts, are very ancient, have been used by generations of foxes, and are reputedly known and available as refuges to all hunted foxes for miles around. Hunting with hounds can never result in the extinction of the present population of foxes, for although perhaps 40,000 or 50,000 are killed annually in Britain – more than 100,000 were killed in Wales and more than 136,000 in Scotland during the years 1949-62 – hunts are responsible for less than a third of these, and their numbers tend to remain more or less static, with a permanent reserve on which to draw from the hills and particularly the impregnable sea-cliff fastnesses. Indeed, were it not for the rather high mortality rate among the juveniles they would be even more numerous, for a litter may contain as many as a dozen cubs. On hill sheep-farms and in deer forests foxes are shot, trapped and poisoned because they kill some lambs and deer calves, though a considerable proportion of casualties among domestic stock attributed to foxes are in actual fact taken as carrion, while their predation on game-birds has very little effect on the overall number of these. But, as Fraser Darling has pointed out, despite this constant harassment the rise and fall of the fox population in the Highlands seems to follow a cycle, possibly extending over a period of twenty years, beyond the control of man. Epidemics of such diseases as mange may temporarily decimate foxes locally, but from these the stock recovers with extraordinary rapidity. On the Continent, however, rabies – which has been recognised in central Europe since early in the nineteenth century – has now spread from Germany into France and almost to the Channel ports. It would be superfluous to speculate on the fate of foxes in particular and of wildlife in general should the virus be carried across the Channel. How easily this could occur is illustrated by the snaring in West Sussex in 1976 of a racoon-dog. Originally an inhabitant of Asian deciduous forests, the squat, somewhat fox-like racoon-dog has been extending its range westwards across Europe for many years. It will be interesting to observe any change of habits in this new environment of an animal that in its eastern habitat preys for preference on fish and amphibians, pouncing on them in shallow waters, and is unique among the members of the Canidae in becoming almost inactive during the winter, emerging only infrequently from its den in a hollow tree or rocks.

10 Deer in the Forest and on the Hill

> Now I shall prove how hunters live in this world more joyfully than any other men. For when the hunter riseth in the morning, and he sees a sweet and fair morn and clear weather and bright, and he heareth the song of the small birds, the which sing so sweetly with great melody and full of love, each in it's own language in the best wise that it can according that it learneth of its own kind. And when the sun is arisen, he shall see fresh dew upon the small twigs and grasses, and the sun by his virtue shall make them shine. And that is great joy and liking to the hunter's heart. After when he shall go to his quest or searching, he shall see or meet anon with the hart without great seeking, and shall harbour him well and readily within a little compass. It is a great joy and liking to the hunter.
>
> *The Master of Game*

Although red deer and roebuck were among the earliest inhabitants of Britain there is only a possibility that fallow deer were also indigenous. It is true that the remains of a species of fallow are associated with an era preceding the final glaciation, but there have been no post-glacial finds of true fallow earlier than those in a few Romano-British refuse heaps at London and Colchester. There is no documentary evidence of their presence in Britain prior to Aelfric's reference in the tenth century to hunting 'bucks' with hounds and chasing them into nets, and to the statement in Domesday Book that fallow deer were frequently enclosed in parks; but it is not unreasonable to infer that it was the Romans who introduced 'ornamental' fallow to Britain from their native haunts in southern Europe, since one would suppose that both Saxons and Danes were too occupied with fighting, farming and colonising to concern themselves with importing deer. A wealthy Roman patrician, subsequently Emperor Gordian I, is in fact reputed to have exhibited two hundred fallow bucks, including some from Britain, at a wild beast spectacular in Rome about AD 238.

Whatever may have been their origins, fallow deer have always been predominantly park deer in Britain, and private fenced or walled parks had begun to replace the royal hunting forests in the thirteenth century, furnishing the aristocracy with a supply of fresh meat with which to supplement their salt beef during the winter months.

According to William Harrison:

> In every shire of England there are great plenty of parks . . . suffice to say that in Kent and Essex only are to the number of an hundred, and twenty in the bishopric of Durham, wherein great plenty of fallow deer . . . Our parks are generally enclosed with strong pales made of oak . . . for the safe keeping of the fallow deer from ranging about the country . . . In times past divers have been fenced in with stone walls, especially in the times of the Romans, who first brought fallow deer into this land (as some conjecture), albeit those enclosures were overthrown again by the Saxons and Danes . . . where no wood is they are also enclosed with piles of slate . . . I find also the circuit of these enclosures . . . oftentimes a walk of four or five miles, and sometimes more or less. Whereby it is seen what a store of ground is employed upon that vain commodity, which bringeth no manner of gain or profit to the owner, sith they commonly give away their flesh.

In his 1617 *Itinerary* Fynes Moryson stated that: 'Every gentleman of five hundredth or a thousand pounds rent by the yeere' had a park for fallow deer, and by the middle of that century there were more than seven hundred such deer parks. Although many of these were broken up during the Civil Wars, there were reputed to be as many as six thousand fallow deer in Grimsthorpe Park about 1780. (There was an old prejudice against keeping different species of deer in the same park.) Descendants of the original park herds of fallow still inhabit such ancient preserves as Epping Forest, the New Forest, Rockingham Forest and Cannock Chase, whilst escapes in the seventeenth century and subsequently have colonised most deciduous and mixed woodlands in England, though being grazers rather than browsers they feed mainly outside the woods. Elsewhere in Britain fallow deer are less widely distributed, since they avoid open moorland and farmland lacking covert; but the fact that they have thrived so vigorously in the wild state in our climate, despite being typically a southern European species, could be advanced as an indication of their being indigenous.

It is surprising how many ecological niches are still available to aliens in our deforested, over-urbanised Britain. During the past hundred years three species of east Asian deer – muntjac or barking deer, sika and water deer – have been introduced or have escaped from parks or zoos, and have succeeded in establishing themselves permanently as wild residents, with sika colonising woods and estuarine reed-beds from southern England to Kerry and Caithness, and the other two species large areas of suburban and rural central England; but the most unlikely additions to the British fauna have been the red-necked wallabies, five of which, together with a small herd of red deer (and a yak!), escaped from a private menagerie near Leek in Staffordshire in the early 1940s. This nucleus increased slowly during the next twenty years to a maximum of forty or fifty dispersed in half a dozen colonies over the heather moors and dense woodland and scrub of the Peak, where they subsisted mainly on the heather and purple moor-grass, though browsing the foliage of pine trees when the snow cover was deep. Although in their home country of Tasmania these wallabies range as high as 3,000 and exceptionally 4,000 feet, the severe winter of 1962-3 in Britain almost wiped out the Peak colonies. Probably fewer than six individuals survived, and since then their increase has been very slow. A few are also at large in the Sussex forests of Ashdown and St Leonard's.

If fallow deer are characteristic of park country, roebuck are almost exclusively a woodland species both in Britain and throughout their Continental range from the Mediterranean to Scandinavia. Their

20. A Wallab

dependence on woodland has, however, been over-emphasised. It is true that no roe deer could survive without having a nearby wood as a base, but in a habitat such as the Scottish Highlands, where every pinewood or birch grove harbours roe, they feed in the bogs and water-meadows and out on the moors almost as often as in the woods, occasionally ranging up into the hills in both summer and winter to heights of 2,000 or 2,500 feet and to two or three miles from the nearest wood. Moreover, where not persecuted, they feed in these exposed places by day as much as by night, for nocturnalism among mammals is often an unnatural condition imposed by man's harassment. During the winter Highland roe pass most of the short hours of daylight feeding out on the moors in family groups or small herds of seven or eight, nibbling at the tips of the heather, browsing among the bog-myrtle in hollows or scraping at the lichens and mosses on knolls from which the wind has swept the snow. From time to time, especially when alarmed, these small groups amalgamate and are joined by the more solitary bucks to form temporary herds, which exceptionally may be twenty strong.

It is difficult to credit that these Highland roe are kin to the shy woodland dwellers south of the Borders, whose diurnal excursions out of the woods tend to be restricted to the early hours of the morning when they are returning to their lairs from their night's feeding. No doubt the boldness of Highland roe is in response to untypically favourable conditions, for the widespread destruction of the forests in all parts of Britain had probably reduced their range by the middle of the eighteenth century to the Highlands, unless some survived in the Border country, and the Lake District. If deforestation is generally held to be responsible for the catastrophic decline in the roe population, it is possible that some other factor was also involved, for during the period 1750-1850 there was a parallel decrease in their numbers in Sweden followed by a similar increase and an enormous extension of their range over the past 125 years. Whereas in 1850 they were present only locally and in small numbers in the extreme south of Sweden, they have now spread at least a thousand miles northwards to southern Lapland, probably as a result of the extermination of the wolves. In the Highlands sufficient forest remained to harbour a nucleus of the indigenous stock. Then, at the end of the eighteenth century the lairds began planting trees around their houses and subsequently, with the vast development of sporting estates, embarked on an extravaganza of planting, with a view to embellishing their estates and lodges, providing covert for game and, at the instigation of the Highland Society, as a long-term investment. By the middle of the nineteenth century these new woods were approaching maturity, and there was further substantial planting towards the end of the century, providing ideal colonising territory for the indigenous roe, though their population explosion – with no wolves to keep their numbers down – dates from the Forestry Commission's planting programme begun in 1919.

21. Fallow Deer

South of the Border numerous introductions, together with re-afforestation, have resulted in some twenty counties in England and much of Wales being recolonised. In densely populated southern England the roe often exist, unobserved by their human neighbours, in small woods isolated in the midst of agricultural or urban zones. According to Richard Prior, who has been studying roe extensively in the New Forest and Cranborne Chase for several years, the most favourable woods are either groves of oak with grassy rides and all around such essential feed as hazel, bramble and the shoots of young trees, or blocks of firs whose down-sweeping branches provide shelter and carpets of needles for couching places. The fact that in such an environment they can multiply at the rate of 30 per cent per annum accounts for their phenomenal increase. It was Prior in England and Kenneth MacArthur in southern Scotland who discovered that much of the damage caused to plantations by roe topping and barking young trees, and also by using them for rubbing the velvet off their new antlers in the early spring, could be avoided by proper management. Their studies of the roe's life history indicated that every tenanted wood is divided up by the various bucks into territories that may cover twenty acres in an oakwood with its abundant undergrowth, but as much as a hundred acres in a pinewood in which undergrowth is either sparse or absent. Territories are demarcated by a buck scraping away the bark from a tree with his short sharp antlers and depositing on the bare patch a secretion from a sweat-gland in his forehead. They are maintained from spring until late summer, and from them the owners chase away intruding bucks, while also relieving tension by horning saplings and bushes. If therefore there are too many bucks in a wood,

2. A Red Deer Stag

there is insufficient territorial space, with the result that the younger bucks are driven out to colonise and damage other vacant woods; while the more bucks there are in a wood the greater is the damage to the trees, over and above that incurred by their feeding on the shoots, because continual territorial invasions by surplus bucks lead to a proportionately greater incidence of tree-horning by irascible owners.

Red deer, unlike the giant deer, were able to adapt to the changes in their environment after the final glaciation, and in post-glacial eras spread throughout the deciduous woodlands of temperate Europe – with the exception of Italy – as far north as the Scottish Highlands and southern Scandinavia. Included in their range were such diverse habitats as the Engadine forest in Switzerland, the wooded steppes of southern Russia and even the remnant groves along the Mediterranean; they also colonised North Africa and parts of Asia. That they were evidently widespread in Britain is indicated by their numerous remains at such prehistoric settlements as Star Carr and the Glastonbury lake-village.

The Pleistocene stag was a very large deer, a third larger than a twentieth-century Highland stag and twice as heavy, with antlers carrying 20 or 22 points; but it was no larger than a modern Caucasus stag, which may reach a weight of almost forty stone, and little larger than the thirty-stone stags of the Carpathians and East Prussian forests. Moreover, if today the average Highland stag weighs only fourteen stone and seldom carries more than 12 points, it must not be forgotten that stags exceeding thirty stone and carrying more than 20 points were being killed in the Highlands as recently as the early nineteenth century, before the trophy hunters began to cull every heavy-antlered stag on the hill.

It is invariably asserted that red deer were exclusively woodland deer until forest clearance forced them to become moor and hill deer; but while this may have been true of those in heavily forested lowland areas it is significant that almost six hundred years ago *The Master of Game* was stating that the deer, after coming down from the hills to rut in the forest and on the heaths and uncultivated lands, would winter in these low-ground localities until April. They then grazed the new growth near farms and villages until the grass was tall, when they returned to graze on the hills, where there were no troublesome flies. Thus, while the Highland deer may originally have passed much of the year in the oak and pine woods browsing on the leaves of such trees and shrubs as aspens, willows, hazels and bramble when the grass was not in season, they certainly always migrated to the hills during the summer months, in order to graze the sweet mountain grasses and sedges and to escape the worst of the flies, which the stags must have found intolerable in the forest when their antlers were in velvet during the early summer months. Even on the hills, however, they would not have been able to evade the attentions of the nostril-flies, despite repeatedly plunging their muzzles into patches of late-lying snow, for these large black and yellow bee-like insects hovered over the deer's heads and ejected droplets of fluid containing larvae into their nostrils.

The difference between then and now is that today the deer may no longer be able to find pine forests or birchwoods in which to shelter during the winter storms, for there are many deer forests in which the wintering glens hold only a few stunted birches straggling up the ravines, with here and there a small rowan. The ubiquitous sheep, by their selective feeding, have literally eaten the heart out of the hills of Scotland – eaten out the sweet grasses and let in the fog and moss and bracken; and not only that, but have also consumed every seedling tree. There are glens that never see a deer, but where sheep winter and where not a sapling birch or alder or hazel can be found to replace the gnarled and ancient groves; and so it was two hundred years ago:

> Everything must make way for the sheep. There is not a single brake now in which a bramble could grow; no tuft of brushwood on the slopes where one could gather a nut; he has shaved the country as smooth and bare as the gable-wall of a house . . . the birds, too, have left us; they have gone to the wood on the other side of the sound; even the grey cuckoo cannot find a single stunted bush where it might lie.

As an eighteenth-century Highland deer-stalker lamented in *A Song of Foxes:*

> Ho! Ho! Ho! the foxes!
> Would there were more of them,
> I'd give heavy gold
> For a hundred score of them!

My blessing with the foxes dwell,
For that they hunt the sheep so well!

Ill fa' the sheep, a grey-faced nation,
That swept our hills with desolation!

And may the young cubs prosper well
Where snug in rocky holes they dwell.

Thus in some 'forests' the deer must survive without the shelter and provender provided by woods in that desperate struggle against starvation in a hard winter, when for weeks at a time their main source of food – mosses and lichens, coarse sedges and young heather – may be buried beneath an iron-hard crust of frozen snow, though even in those conditions they can break through the crust overlaying bushy heather, or thrust their long heads in at an angle beneath it. But rather than the shelter of the woods it is the presence or absence of extensive tracts of long heather that is the critical factor, for the heather forms a protective shield over mosses and berry-plants. Hence the attraction of those corries filled with old belly-deep heather, while if the 'forest' does include pine woods then there is good feeding on the no less luxuriant growth of blaeberry. Nevertheless, so well have Highland red deer adapted to life in the hills that when the sun is up on a frosty winter's morning, companies of stags, a hundred strong, will climb up from a pine wood, in which they have passed the night, to a height of 2,000 or 3,000 feet on the white hills. All day their black clumps lace the snow, as they bask in the sun or scrape away at lichens or fringe-moss on exposed stony flats, swept almost bare of snow by strong winds. Although there is still ample fodder of blaeberry and heather in the glen, they prefer to climb to the tops for these dry and desiccated lichens. Indeed, the high places appear to hold some psychological attraction for the stags, for on other days it is the late afternoon before they climb up out of the corries to enjoy the last half-hour of sunshine that lingers on the tops after the strath has been plunged into cold shadow.

Although under present conditions half the summer's stock of calves die, and one-sixth of the stags and a lesser proportion of hinds are culled, the red deer not only maintain their strength but increase. Today, after a series of open winters, their numbers in Scotland are probably at a peak of 200,000, despite the fact that they suffer their heaviest mortality from the ravages of such internal parasites as lungworm and liver-fluke during winters of incessant rains. Yet by the end of the eighteenth century only nine of the ancient deer forests in the Highlands had not been taken over in whole or part by sheep and black cattle, and there were no deer left in the Lowlands. Indeed, in addition to the Highlands, probably only the Lake District in north England, and Exmoor, the Quantocks and the Brendon hills in the south, together with a part of County Kerry in Ireland, still held mainly indigenous stocks of red deer, though they subsequently spread to or were introduced to many other parts of Britain. The clan chieftains had hunted the deer for centuries. From the enterprising John Taylor, the Water Poet, we learn in 1618 that:

> For once in the yeere, which is the whole moneth of August, and sometimes part of September, many of the nobility and gentry of the Kingdome (for their pleasure) doe come into these high-land countries to hunt . . . The manner of the hunting is this: Five or sixe hundred men doe rise early in the morning, and they doe disperse themselves divers wayes, and seven, eight or tenne miles compasse, they doe bring or chase the deere in many heards (two, three or foure hundred) to such or such a place . . ., then when day is come, the Lords and gentlemen . . . doe ride . . . to the said places, sometimes wading up to the middles through bournes and rivers . . . and doe lye downe on the ground, till those foresaid scouts, which are called the Tenckhell, doe bring downe the deere . . . Then after we had stayed there three houres or thereabouts, we might perceive the deere appeare on the hills round about us (their heads making a shew like a wood), which being closely followed by the tenckhell, are chased downe into the valley where we lay; then all the valley on each side being way-laid with a hundred couple of strong Irish grey-hounds, they are let loose . . . upon the heard of deere, that with dogges, gunnes, arrowes, durkes, and daggers, in the space of two houres, fourscore fat deere were slain.

However, the vastness of the Highlands enabled the deer to survive the medieval chase. Then, in the nineteenth century many of the wealthier lairds began to clear the sheep from their land and speculate in sporting estates on which deer could be stalked and grouse driven. At the same time the northward extension of the railway to Perth in 1849, Inverness in 1861 and Thurso in 1874 brought the Highlands within comfortable reach of the English aristocracy and gentry, whose interest in the sporting potentialities (with the new breech-loader) of the Highlands, and in their fashionably romantic landscape, was aroused by the publication of a succession of books. The first of these, published in 1804 – six years before Sir Walter Scott's *The Lady of the Lake* and ten years before *Waverley* – was Colonel Thomas Thornton's *A Sporting Tour through the Northern Parts of England and Great Parts of the Highlands of Scotland*. This described with an abundance of local colour his shooting, hawking and fishing adventures in the Kingussie locality of Strathspey during the summer and autumn of 1786 – he had been acquainted with the Highlands for ten or twelve years before that – and included an account of landing by a somewhat unethical means a 5 feet 4½ inches pike weighing about 48 pounds from Loch Alvie. No author was better calculated to publicise the Highlands in the grand manner to his contemporaries than this immensely rich and colourful Yorkshire squire and regular soldier who, when a Master of Staghounds in the south of England, arrived for a meet in Epping Forest accompanied by a bevy of fair ladies (dressed, like himself, in scarlet) in a barouche drawn by four cream-coloured Arabians. He was also one of the most extravagant gamblers of his day, laying 10,000 guineas on his hound bitch Merkin to run five miles over Newmarket against any hound of her year, giving two hundred yards' start; was the most proficient falconer of his time; and was an outstanding athlete, performing such acts of showmanship as walking four miles in 32 minutes, jumping six five-barred gates in six minutes and then repeating this feat on horseback, and galloping down and picking up a hare from his horse.

By the 1840s, when another sportsman, John Colquhoun, published *The Moor and the Loch* and the Stuart brothers their *Lays of the Deer Forest*, there had already been an enormous increase in the numbers of red deer because of the high rents being paid for well-stocked deer forests; and interest in the sporting possibilities of the Highlands was further stimulated by the publication during the same decade of William Scrope's *Days of Deer Stalking*, in which he gave an account of ten years' stalking in the Forest of Atholl with his deer-hounds, those superb dogs with –

An eye of sloe, with ear not low
With horse's breast, and depth of chest
With breadth of loin, and curve in groin,
And nape set far behind the head . . .

In contrast to Thornton's militarily conducted safaris of guests and retainers, equipped with horses and boats and amply supplied with a variety of choice foods and drinks, Scrope stalked alone or with one or two native Highlanders as companions on the hill. His book gave an unexpectedly massive boost to the purchase at sky-high prices of deer forests and grouse moors by American millionaires and Sassenach tycoons alike, anxious to jump on the bandwagon of those enjoying this new prestigious sport; though by 1890 Scrope's method of hunting with deer-hounds had been almost wholly superseded by stalking with the express rifle. More shooting lodges were erected by the lairds, and stalking had become economically important in the Highlands. By the advent of the First World War sheep-farming had been suppressed in two hundred deer forests, and today some landowners are tentatively exploring the practicability of ranching deer for venison.

11 Of Small Mice More than a Thousand

House Mice

The widespread dispersals of the pre-Roman Iron Age peoples over Europe must have resulted in the transportation, deliberate or accidental, into new localities of a number of small mammals that had become adapted to man-made habitats and in some cases had become commensal with man. It must be considered a fair probability that it was at this time that house mice arrived in Britain by boat, and the recent discovery of two subfossil fragments in Dorset may confirm this. They may possibly have originated in Mediterranean lands or North Africa, but most probably on the steppes east of the Volga. There, on the borders of Russian Turkestan and the Iranian plateau, wheat and barley have been cultivated since Neolithic times, and house mice still live in a 'wild' state. In Britain they would have had access to ample supplies of food in the form of grain, which the early agriculturalists stored for household use in deep chalk-pits lined with basketry or skins, and retained for seed in small square granaries raised above the ground. However, there is no definite reference to mice in Britain until the time of Alfred the Great; but they were evidently well-established by the twelfth century, for in the *Lambeth Homilies* (1175) we read that: 'When a man will bait his mouse-trap he binds thereupon the treacherous cheese and roasteth it so that it should smell sweetly; and through the sweet smell of the cheese, he enticeth many a mouse into his trap.'

In due course British house mice established themselves not only in towns but in fields and on small islands such as Skokholm, the Isle of May and the larger Hebrides. The latter included remote St Kilda, to which they may have been shipped at a very early date, for it has been claimed that St Kilda, like the Orkney Isles, was settled by late Neolithic seafarers from Iberia and France or by Azilian fowlers from the Hebrides, though the earliest references to it, as Hirtir (the Island of Gloom?) occurs in a thirteenth-century Icelandic saga.

Although there may be colonies of mice on arable land at some distance from human habitation, these usually have farm buildings as headquarters, and in Britain they have always remained basically dependent on man. There is, for example, a true rural population of house mice: a small one in the fields and a larger one centred on the farm steadings; and during the summer months they may be as numerous in some districts as bank voles and half as numerous as long-tailed field mice. Prior to the introduction of combine harvesters this rural population lived in the unthreshed corn stacks that stood in the fields or stackyards. A single stack might house more than two thousand mice, consuming fourteen pounds of grain a day, and some 16 per cent of Britain's grain harvest was eaten or spoilt by these mice; for a stack provided all their requirements – shelter, food, nest material, an even temperature and protection from predators. It was not even necessary for them to leave the stack for water, since the grain contained enough moisture to satisfy the greater part of their needs and the balance was supplied by dew or by rain falling on the outside of the stack, when all its inhabitants would 'surface' to drink. The ideal nature of this habitat is indicated by the fact that stack mice reared more than ten litters a year, almost twice as many as urban mice. Since there are on an average five young to a litter, and since the latter are sexually mature when only six or eight weeks old and may themselves be producing young by the middle of July, it will be seen that a population of mice can increase ten- or fifteen-fold by the autumn. Add to their fecundity their remarkable adaptability to environment, and it is evident that house mice can never be exterminated; for what can one do with an animal that can survive and also breed in the total darkness of a cold meat store in a temperature of 15°F, subsisting exclusively on frozen meat and making nests of the hessian in which the meat is wrapped or of the fur and feathers from the carcases, or actually burrowing into the carcases? Only the complete evacuation of the human population from Britain might prove fatal to the mice. On Hirta, the main island of St Kilda, for example, house mice were described as prolific. They inhabited most of the houses except the post office, and also the dykes and dry-stone *cleitean* or store-chambers, and overlapped the long-tailed field mice's niche in the village meadows; but they never adapted to a wild existence as they have done in the Faeroes, to which they were probably introduced not much more than a thousand years ago, and where on some of the outlying islands they live in the great bird cliffs and may possibly hibernate in the winter. By 1931, however, only one year after the human population had been evacuated from St Kilda, trapping indicated that possibly only two dozen house mice remained on Hirta, concentrated in two houses that still contained some stores of food. The rest may have been killed by feral cats before they could adjust to a diet of natural rather than human provender; but as Kenneth Williamson has pointed out in *St Kilda Summer*, the evacuation deprived them not only of food but of warmth in the cottages and byres. The winter following the exodus must have been critical for them, as they adapted to new conditions and were obliged to forage further afield for food and lose body heat in so doing. They would also have had to compete for food with the more robust field mice, which by 1938 – when no house mice could be located – had taken over the latter's domain in the village and had become very numerous both without and within the deserted houses, and remained so despite the establishment on Hirta in 1957 of a radar tracking station for the South Uist rocket range.

Field Mice

Although the long-tailed field mice are also known as wood mice, since they are characteristic inhabitants of deciduous woods throughout Europe, including the Mediterranean lands, they yet thrive on the treeless moors of such islands as St Kilda, the Shetlands and Iceland, exploiting a typical vole niche that the voles have not colonised. In Shetland indeed the field mice occupy every type of habitat from house to hills, and on a moonlight winter night have been seen feeding in numbers on the carcase of a grey seal washed up on the sands. It has been suggested that during the initial mammalian colonisation of Britain in one of the inter-glacial periods populations of mice, voles and shrews may have become isolated on small islands and have eventually evolved into recognisable sub-species; and that among these were the St Kilda field mice, which are distinguished by being almost twice the weight of those on the Highland mainland and are also tinged with buff on the underparts instead of being pure grey in colour – the St Kilda house mice were also 15 or 20 per cent heavier than those on the mainland. It is possible that the ice-sheet terminated in a barrier off the Outer Hebrides, with the result that St Kilda escaped complete glaciation, and that its field mice – and also its wrens – may have been in continuous occupation of the island since an inter-glacial era of birch, alder and hazel. At a later date they would find shelter in the hundreds of man-made *cleitean* dotted about the three islands they inhabit. But if the ice-sheet off the Long Island included St Kilda, then it seems improbable that such small mammals could have a survived a glacial period; while, as G. B. Corbet has suggested, it is unlikely that such archipelagoes as the Hebrides, Orkney and Shetland could have become joined to the mainland after the last ice age because the northern half of Britain was depressed by the enormous weight of the ice-sheet, and rose only slowly after the ice melted. It would seem, therefore, that most small island mammals have, like the house mice, been introduced by human agency.

Harvest Mice

There is no definitive evidence that the mechanisation of agriculture, which has reduced the rural population of house mice, was also responsible during the earlier decades of this century for the decline in the numbers and range of the harmless little harvest mice. Since the latter

23. A Harvest Mouse on its Nest

do not inhabit Scandinavia, they reach the northern limits of their range in Britain, where they are now relatively common only in south and east England, though they appear to have increased again during the past seventy years. It is true that they are reported to have become extinct in the Weald after the introduction of close-cutting reaping machines, which destroyed the nursery nests suspended in the corn; and when corn-stacks were a feature of arable farms, they regularly wintered in these, often sharing a stack with house mice in a ratio of one to ten, but not if rats were also present. Gilbert White, who added the harvest mice to the British fauna list – though they had in fact been previously identified by George Montagu – recorded upwards of a hundred under the thatch of an oat-stack. On the other hand White observed that they might also winter in deep earth-burrows lined with grass, and when corn-stacks became obsolete in Devon they both wintered and nested in small colonies in the earth-bank hedges and undergrowth. Some naturalists believe that they will survive as long as there are hedges, though this would depend on the future agricultural policy in regard to the removal of the rank herbage fringing fields, the cultivation of overgrown field corners, and the use of pesticides. Although harvest mice have exploited for some centuries the ideal environment provided by cornfields (preferably those including thistles!) in which to nest and corn-stacks in which to winter, farmland is not in fact their natural habitat, for they are specialised inhabitants of the 'stalk zone' of such plants as cereals, reeds, hogweed, mugwort and willowherb. Among these they manoeuvre most dexterously, steadying themselves by winding partially prehensile tails around a stem or extending them as balancing organs while swarming up the tallest and slenderest stalk. In East Anglia, for example, they are, according to E. A. Ellis in his book *The Broads*, regular inhabitants not only of cornfields, but also of most fens where tall vegetation surrounds broads, and are often abundant where purple small-reed, reed canary-grass, reed and great pond sedge grow. They construct their summer nests of the shredded and interwoven leaves of these plants, collecting and eating the fluffy seeds of the reeds in winter, and use as temporary refuges the branches of reeds that are stacked on ponds and river-banks from January to April.

Dormice

The present status of dormice also presents problems, and their geographical distribution is most puzzling. Pockets of the common or hazel dormice are dotted about deciduous woods with secondary growth in the south of England and southern Sweden, but there are none in Denmark; while the much larger, fat or edible dormice are not found anywhere in Scandinavia, nor in the coastal regions of northern France, but since being introduced to the Chilterns as long ago as 1902 have established themselves in that one area only of about a hundred square miles around Tring, where thirty or forty are caught every year. In an

24. A Dormouse

article in *Animals*, Maurice Burton has attempted to account for the restricted range and numbers of the common dormice, which have certainly decreased since the time, fifty years ago, when they were common children's pets, and from the middle of last century when Yarrell described finding colonies of ten or a dozen or more nests in thickets of shrubs well away from human habitation. Since they are the most arboreal of the mice, and nocturnal, with their typical environment the green canopy of a hazel bush, Burton has suggested that they enjoy greater security than most small mammals during the summer months. The diurnal sleeping nest is generally built in a bush or in the fork of a sapling, though sometimes under a tussock of grass, and the female's breeding nest, which is twice as large, is in a bramble or small bush. Both are usually a few feet above the ground and not easily accessible to predators from below or above. Moreover, when feeding at night on the seed-crops of beeches, hazels or sweet chestnuts, they clamber about the tangle of slender branches and twigs, where they are fairly safe from owls. Since the female sites her nest in a hedge at some distance from her woodland headquarters, the widespread uprooting of hedgerows may be one factor that has affected the dormice's distribution.

They hibernate, usually singly, from as early as October in a strong rain-proof nest of leaves and moss, bound with honeysuckle bark and lined with shredded bark, placed in a hollow tree stump, in a mossy hole in the ground at the base of a hazel sapling, or deep beneath the leaf litter. But if, asks Burton, their winter quarters were in actual fact so secure and their summer activities fraught with so little danger, as seems likely, then we would have to explain why dormice are not much more common than they are, particularly since several litters of young are born every year: 'The answer seems to be that winter is the period when they are most at risk . . . The dormouse has to come down to ground level, and its fibrous nest . . . is no protection against hungry predators, such as magpies, crows, foxes, badgers, stoats, weasels and possibly rats; and four out of every five dormice die during the hibernatory period:

> The paradox is that the dormouse should have evolved such a refined mechanism for ensuring successful hibernation to tide over a period of possible food shortage. The net result of it all is to make the species still liable to the heavy winter mortality which is suffered by non-hibernating rodents.

It has been asserted (with some exaggeration) that the universal decimation of predators has resulted in so great an increase in the numbers of mice and voles over the past hundred years that it is now almost impossible for an English woodland to regenerate naturally because seedling trees are destroyed by being barked during the first year or two of growth. Moreover, in recent decades the Forestry Commission's plantings have provided thousands of ideal rodent habitats. In 1914 there were 3 million acres of broad-leaved trees in Britain to half a million acres of conifers, but the ratio is now 1¾ million acres of broad-leaved to 2¾ million acres of conifers. This conversion has presumably increased Britain's rodent population by hundreds of thousands or by millions.

Voles

Plagues of voles have been recorded in Britain on a number of occasions. There was one in Essex in 1580, associated with an invasion of short-eared owls, and there were two major plagues on the upland sheep-walks of the Scottish Border country, particularly Eskdalemuir, in 1874-6 and 1891-3. Because there are no records of similar plagues on the Borders earlier that century these two in the last quarter have been attributed to the indiscriminate slaughter of predators. But what control do predators in fact exercise over rodents? The vole likely to occur in plague proportions in Britain is the short-tailed species (*Microtus agrestis*), whose normal population density is less than fifty to the acre, but which builds up to ten times that number at the peak of a cycle every four or, less frequently, three years, and to vastly more during a plague. During the build-up the numbers of predatory mammals and especially birds increase in the stricken area, and the most characteristic of these are the short-eared owls, which are so dependent on adequate supplies of voles that they may not be able to rear full complements of young without them.

The breeding success of some kestrels and barn owls also fluctuates cyclically with the abundance of this vole, for a pair of barn owls may catch considerably more than three thousand small mammals, over half of them voles, during the course of a year. The decline in the British population of barn owls has, however, been caused by the use of toxic chemicals, by changes in farming techniques and the destruction of hedgerows resulting in the displacement of rodents, and by the ever-increasing scarcity of suitable nesting sites due to the neglect and demolition of old barns. As Roger Hosking has pointed out in *Wildlife*, there are still old cob and stone barns in the West Country, many of them more than two hundred years old, whose builders seem to have had barn owls especially in mind, in constructing open windows for easy access, thick walls in which to nest, and oak beams on which to roost; but their replacements tend to be asbestos sheds lacking any nesting facilities. Moreover, the owls cannot tolerate the noise of

25. A Short-tailed Field Vole

modern farm machinery or too much human disturbance, deserting barns in which milk refrigerator motors are operating day and night.

To return to the vole plague on the Borders in 1891-3, which was the most catastrophic recorded and resulted in almost half of 30,000 acres of sheep pasture in Roxburghshire alone being destroyed and riddled with burrows and runways. During the build-up the voles swarmed over the low-ground sheep-walks, infesting an area some sixty miles long and from twelve to twenty miles wide. One farmer killed 13,000 with a spade-like implement on 3,000 acres of sheep-walk in three months, another 15,000 in one month, and a third with twelve terriers accounted for from 400 to 600 a day. In the autumn of 1891 numbers of short-eared owls, and also long-eared owls, kestrels, buzzards, rooks and black-headed gulls, together with stoats and weasels, arrived. Subsequently, several hundred short-eared owls nested without intermission from February – when one female, sitting on eggs in the snow, had 17 dead voles around her, and another 37 deposited by the males – until September, and averaged ten or twelve eggs to the clutch. Robert Service has described how at midsummer 1892, when the plague was at its peak, he was out on the hills at midnight:

> The night was bright and clear, and very still. The owls were on all sides flying like no other birds I ever saw. The voles were scurrying hither and thither, squeaking and rustling as one stepped over and amongst them. The unfeathered owlets had left their nests, and were sitting blinking their eyes and contorting their heads in groups on almost every little hillock. The parents never troubled to alight amongst their offspring, they simply flew past, and flung the dead voles at their young in their by-going . . .

But although laboratory tests suggest that one short-eared owl may take between 700 and 2,000 voles in the course of a year, the effect of owl predation on a population of voles must be negligible; and it has been estimated that even a concentration of some hundreds of owls in a plague area is unlikely to account for more than from two to five hundredths of one per cent of the voles daily. The extermination of their natural predators may possibly assist a vole population to explode to plague numbers, but the main factor must, as in the case of lemmings, be the coincidence of their natural cyclical increase with a series of exceptionally favourable feeding and breeding seasons. It is possible that the extensive afforestation in Scotland during the nineteenth century also contributed to the Border plagues, in as much as the short-tailed vole thrives in an undisturbed forestry environment of grass and rush in which the herbage is not burnt and which is fenced off from grazing and trampling by sheep and cattle. It is in this newly fenced and planted ground that the short-eared owls breed most numerously in the wide expanses of rough grassland and rolling moors of south-west Scotland, until the growing tree cover kills off the undergrowth after some fifteen years.

As inevitably as a vole population explodes, so does it crash, and though the Border owls nested again in 1893, the bulk of the voles had already disappeared by then, and hundreds of young owls died: 68 of them, together with 8 adult owls, being found in a fox's earth, for foxes appear to prey heavily on both young and old owls and also take their eggs. Although the young owls were in what Service described as the last stages of emaciation he believed that this was not due to starvation, but to being fed with diseased voles. However, a vole crash is probably not brought about by disease or parasitic infection, or by the toll taken by predators, or by starvation, because there is invariably some vegetation left in an infested area, though this may perhaps have been rendered inedible by the general fouling of the ground; but as in the case of lemmings, again, by the psychological stress of overcrowding which induces physiological changes that result in aggressive behaviour and actual fighting, in the killing and eating of new-born litters, and in the actual inability to breed.

12 Their Houses Rats Possess

Rats, like house mice, reached Britain accidentally by ship, though much later than mice. It is generally agreed that Giraldus' account of St Yvorus cursing rats and expelling them from a province in Leinster in the fifth century in fact referred to mice. However, his actual words were: From this district the larger species of mice, commonly called rats, were so entirely expelled by the curse of St Yvorus . . . that none were afterwards bred there.' And it is significant, since Giraldus was a Welshman, that the Welsh language does not include a word for rat, which is known as big mouse.

Black Rats

The black rats, which were the first of their kind to arrive in Britain, originated in the hot climate of south-east Asia, where they often existed in country remote from human habitation, and where they were of a reddish-brown colour with white or pale-yellow underparts; but as they colonised westwards to Asia Minor, North Africa and southern Europe and became increasingly commensal with man, so, as in the case of house mice, darker colour-phases developed. Since they were unknown to the Greeks and also to the Romans it is possible that they reached the West in the Crusaders' ships early in the twelfth century, though there is no contemporary evidence or even folklore to this effect. The first mention of them in western Europe – other than unconfirmed reports of their presence at ancient sites in Switzerland – was again by Giraldus, who reported from the Isle of Inisglvair off County Mayo that:

> The larger mice that are commonly called rats swarm in vast numbers in other parts of Ireland, here not a single one is found . . . the small kind swarm to such an amazing degree that they consume more enormous quantities of grain than anywhere else, and are very destructive to clothes.

Four hundred years later Fynes Moryson, who was Secretary to the Lord Deputy of Ireland and travelled around Europe for ten years, quoted a doggerel:

> For four vile beasts Ireland hath no fence:
> Their bodies lice, their houses rats possess:
> Most wicked priests govern their conscience,
> And ravening wolves do waste their fields no less.

During the course of the Middle Ages the black rats spread to towns and villages in many parts of Britain. William Langland refers in his fourteenth-century *Vision of Piers Plowman* to a 'route of ratones and smale mys mo than a thousand'; and in Chaucer's *Pardonere's Tale* we read:

26. A Black Rat

And forth he goeth, no lenger would he tary,
In to the toun unto a Pothecary,
And praied him that he him wolde sell,
Som poison, that he might his ratouns quell.

The impact of these black rats on the well-being and economy of the human inhabitants of Britain was catastrophic, for they were, as we have seen, responsible for the Black Death which began in 1348 and continued to break out sporadically until the Great Plague in 1665. A disease, referred to as the Plague, is also mentioned during Cadwalader's reign in the sixth century; but there is no indication as to whether it was bubonic plague. If it was, then it would support Giraldus' fable of rats being present in Ireland at that time. In a minor, but perhaps more directly pathetic incident, the black rats were also responsible for depopulating the island of North Rona, some fifty miles off the most northerly mainland of Scotland, of its thirty human inhabitants soon after 1685. In *A Description of the Western Islands of Scotland* Martin Martin relates how he was told by the minister of Barvas, of whose glebe Rona was a part, that:

> About 14 Years ago a swarm of Rats, but none knows how, came into *Rona,* and in a short time ate up all the Corn on the Island. In a few Months after some Seamen Landed there, who Robbed the poor People of their Bull. These misfortunes and the want of supply from *Lewis* for the space of a Year, occasion'd the death of all that Ancient Race of People. The Steward of *St Kilda* being by a Storm driven in there, told me that he found a Woman with her Child on her Breast, both lying dead at the side of a Rock: Some Years after, the Minister (to whom the Island belongeth) sent a new Colony to this Island, with suitable Supplies. The following Year a Boat was sent to them with some more supplies and Orders to receive the Rents, but the Boat being lost as is supposed, I can give no further account of this late Plantation.

But even rats could not survive on this small island, once they had eaten up all the barley meal stored in sheep-skins in the Islanders' semi-subterranean houses of dry-stone banked with earth, because the immense ocean swell prevented them from scavenging the rocks in the intertidal zone, and they also starved.

With the invasion of western Europe early in the eighteenth century by the aggressive, more adaptable and more prolific brown rats, the black, presumably unable to compete with them, began to decline. By the end of that century they were virtually extinct in Ireland, though still present in Dublin in the 1860s. By that time they had also become rare in other parts of Britain, being restricted mainly to old houses in cities such as London and Edinburgh, but surviving in some rural parts of Cheshire and north Wales until the 1880s, in Yarmouth until 1895, and on such islands as Lundy, Benbecula and South Ronaldshay. As recently as the last war there were still about four times as many black rats as brown in the Port of London, but today, apart from Lundy and the Channel Islands, they are confined to sea-ports and a few of those inland towns that were formerly connected to ports by canals. In Scandinavia, Finland and Denmark they are still largely limited to ports, though common in urban areas in other parts of Europe.

Black rats are essentially indoor rats, living in warehouses and other high buildings, and there is no evidence that they have ever inhabited fields or hedgerows or corn-stacks. As A. R. Smith, official rat-catcher to Princess Amelia, wrote in 1768 in *The Universal Directory for Taking Alive and Destroying Rats and All Other Kinds of Four-footed and Winged Vermin in a Method Hitherto Unattempted: Calculated for the Use of the Gentleman, the Farmer and the Warrener*:

> The black ones do not burrow and run into shores as the others do but chiefly lie in the ceilings and wainscots in houses, and in outhouses they lie under the ridge tiles, and behind the rafters, and run about the side-plates: but their numbers are greatly diminished to what they were formerly, not many of them being now left, for the Norway rats always drive them out and kill them wherever they can come at them; as a proof of which I was once exercising my employment at a gentleman's house, and when the night came that I appointed to catch, I set all my traps going as usual, and in the lower part of the house in the cellars I caught the Norway rats, but in the upper part of the house I took nothing but black rats. I put them together into a great cage to keep them alive till the morning . . . when the Norway rats killed the black rats immediately and devoured them in my presence.

Brown Rats

The brown rats never occupied tall buildings, and are not restricted to any specialised habitat or food, being more resistant to cold and 'hard living' than the black. Some live in sewers and mines: others live out of doors all the year round in many parts of Britain, and are particularly suited to dry hedgerows where the soil is not compressed, where there are tree roots to nest under, and which are surrounded for most of the year by good cover from such predators as foxes, stoats, weasels, otters, mink and owls. This is important, for in Ireland, where there are fewer species of small rodents than in other parts of Britain, rats may compose as much as 17 per cent of a fox's food, 30 per cent of a barn owl's and 20 per cent of a long-eared owl's.

The brown rats, like the black, originated in Asia, but in the harsh environment of the steppes, possibly as far east as China and Mongolia, and began to erupt from their homelands early in the eighteenth century. Their westward migrations appear in some instances at least to have been set in motion by natural phenomena. After an earthquake in 1727, for instance, hordes of rats crossed the Volga – they are good swimmers – though this is one of the rivers that normally form a barrier to westward migration through the Kazakh corridor from the steppes. The western seaboard of Europe, however, was invaded by sea, with one batch reaching Denmark on a Russian ship at some date prior to 1716 and others, possibly also in Russian ships from the Baltic, the Dublin area of Ireland about 1722 and England in 1730. It will be noted that both black and brown rats were recorded in Ireland before England, and within seven years of their arrival in Ireland the latter were already considered a dangerous pest. In 1729 the editor of Walsh's *Impartial Newsletter* printed the following account of the brown rats in the Merrion district near Dublin:

> This morning we have an account . . . that a parcel of those outlandish Marramounts which are called Mountain Rats, who are now here, grow very common; that they walk in droves and do a great deal of mischief – the writer describes how they ate a woman and nurse child in Merrion. People killed several who are as big as Katts and Rabbits. This part of the country is infested with them. Likewise we hear from Rathfarnham that the like vermin destroyed a little girl in the Field; they are to be seen like rabbits, and are so impudent that they suck the cows – nay abundance of them are to be seen in Fleet Street.

Rats may not suck cows, but there have in fact been a number of reports of them eating people in various parts of the world, including one in the USA in 1903; and Bell relates in *A History of British Quadrupeds* that in a coal-pit, near Killingworth, in which many horses were employed rats, which fed upon the fodder provided for the horses, accumulated in great numbers:

> It was customary in holiday times to bring to the surface the Horses and the fodder, and to close the pit for the time. On one occasion when the holiday had extended to ten days or a fortnight, during which the Rats had been deprived of food, on reopening the pit, the first man who descended was attacked by the starving multitude, and speedily killed and devoured.

The new hedges of the Enclosures may have facilitated the dispersal of brown rats over England, for there is no mention of them in rural areas before 1762 when, in a letter in August of that year from near the port of Holyhead, the writer describes how: 'On Monday last, I had three men reaping all my corn, and not a little trouble did we have; Norwegian rats devouring it standing.' Subsequently, the rats invaded the cornfields in their thousands when the grain was ripening, and after it had been harvested the fields might be dotted with mounds of earth like mole-hills, in which the rats had stored the grain shaken from the ears by strong winds. In the days when the corn was stacked before threshing more than five hundred rats might winter in a single stack, and they were estimated to consume more than seven hundredweight of grain from the average rick. Although much reduced in numbers by control measures during the last war, remnants of brown rat concentrations have always been able to build up a tolerance of such sophisticated poisons as 'Warfarin', and there are now totally immune populations in the west Midlands, Wales and Scotland, and also in Denmark.

13 Rabbits on the Downs, Frogs in the Marshes

The most successful colonising animals are those able to take maximum advantage of man's urban or rural environments, and are therefore most destructive to his economy – mice, rats, squirrels and rabbits. Yet rabbits, oddly enough, do not appear to have thrived in their country of origin, which was Iberia – and possibly also southern France, Corsica and the Balearics; and their dispersal to the uttermost ends of the earth was initiated by the Romans who, after they had been introduced to Italy in the first century BC, reared them for food in walled enclosures, as they also did hares. From these *leporaria* some rabbits escaped by digging under the walls. Others were raised on small islands in various parts of Europe, but not apparently in Britain, for not only is there no old English or Celtic name for them, but no mention of them either in Roman or Saxon Britain or indeed in Domesday Book, though on the Continent the Normans confined them in warrens as a food crop. Although they were probably introduced from France to both England and Scotland late in the eleventh century there is, apart from Giraldus' comparison of Irish hares with them, no historical reference to rabbits in Britain until 1176 when, according to John Sheail's monumentally researched *Rabbits and Their History*, a few were landed on the Isles of Scilly and formed a breeding colony. They must also have been well-established on Lundy at an early date, for between the years 1183 and 1219 the tenant of the island was entitled to take fifty rabbits a year from certain *choris* , and by 1274 five thousand skins were being exported annually. It is perhaps significant that the Lords of the Manor of Lundy, the de Mariscos, had connections with Spain. Warrens were also being protected in Scotland early in the thirteenth century, and the stock for these was probably supplied by the monastery on the Isle of May, which had been founded before the middle of the previous century. In those days rabbits were known as coneys (from the Norman-French), and rabbit or rabbette did not come into use until the fourteenth century, and then only in reference to the young.

Rabbits were introduced to Britain initially as a food crop and confined in warrens, of which by the sixteenth century there may have been more dotted about the length and breadth of England than anywhere else in Europe. 'As for warrens of conies, I judge them almost innumerable', wrote Harrison; and Gesner, in commenting on the vast numbers of rabbits, contrasted their habitat with that of the parched hill and rock country in their native Spain. But during the eighteenth and nineteenth centuries rabbit farming became a commercial proposition, with single warrens harvesting as many as 29,000 rabbits annually, and rabbits were also preserved as game – as were hares in enclosures surrounded by brick walls ten feet high. In the more depressed agricultural areas rabbit warrens even displaced sheep-walks, but the majority of warrens were sited on unproductive land, such as the then sterile sandy wastes of the East Anglian Brecklands. Some of the latter were enormous, extending to three thousand acres enclosed by sod-walls eight miles long. However, innumerable rabbits escaped from these inefficiently fenced warrens and founded wild colonies in a wide variety of habitats, since they could burrow as effectively in the heaviest loams and clays, and even into coal seams, as in light soils. In the favourable environment provided by the Enclosures, by deer parks and fox coverts, and by the extermination of their natural predators – the foxes, wild cats, martens and polecats, and the eagles, kites and buzzards that were trapped at the warrens – the wild rabbit population multiplied at a phenomenal rate during the nineteenth century, reaching an estimated fifty million by the outbreak of the Second World War, and between sixty and a hundred million by the early 1950s. By 1940 they had, after more than eight hundred years, colonised most parts of Britain. They had reached the Hebrides before the end of the seventeenth century, and the northern Highlands during the next century, assisted by such landowners as Osgood MacKenzie's grandfather who imported them to Wester Ross, and thereby provided the hard-pressed wild cats, martens and buzzards with additional prey; but they had not quite completed their conquest of Scotland when further colonisation was halted by the spread of myxomatosis during the years 1953-5.

The rabbit population explosion was effected in spite of the fact that probably few live longer than twelve months, for the rabbit possesses a built-in birth-control mechanism that comes into operation when excessive overcrowding results in continuous psychological stress and a shortage of nutritious plant food. This mechanism prevents the birth of 60 per cent or more of the litters conceived and restricts the potentially prodigious fertility of a doe to ten or twelve young a year, of which predators account for possibly 90 per cent within a few months of their birth. However, a density as high as fifteen or twenty rabbits to the acre in the most heavily infested areas literally changed the landscape in many parts of Britain. Not only did the rabbits destroy one of every fifteen acres of winter wheat, but they cropped the grass pastures of sheep and cattle so closely that the herbage was shorn to less than an inch in height and the lateral buds removed. The result was that little regeneration of grasses was possible and valuable strains and also clover were progressively extirpated, to be replaced by non-nutritious plants and ultimately, in wetter districts, by a carpet of mosses which the rabbits themselves did not eat. In hill country berry-plants were similarly eradicated and replaced by mosses and lichens, while large areas of downland were cropped too closely for sheep to graze, as was also the case on the sandy soils of the Brecklands, where heath was converted into a dwarf heath-fescue grassland. Moreover, although the rabbits nibbled at and reduced the acreage of gorse, they did not eat bracken, thereby facilitating the spread of that highly successful but undesirable fern over areas in which they had destroyed other plants.

The ecology of the south country downs was especially affected by the rabbits, as A. G. Tansley has described in *Britain's Green Mantle:*

> Rabbits never go further for their food than they need, so that the ground surrounding an isolated group of burrows on a chalk down shows a concentric zonation. Immediately around the burrows there is a ring of bare chalk stones thrown out by the vigorous hind feet, then a wide zone of turf eaten down to half an inch or less, grading to herbage less severely nibbled, while at a distance of a hundred yards or so there may be little evidence of rabbit grazing. Where the groups of burrows are numerous the grazing ranges overlap, and in such a region many hundreds of acres might be rendered useless for sheep or cattle. Within the devastated area no seedling of a woody plant could survive, and any scrub that might have been present before the rabbit infestation became overwhelming had its lower branches eaten bare up to the height a rabbit could reach . . . Much of the damage that rabbits inflict on shrubs and young trees arises not from what they eat but from the need to wear down their continuously growing teeth, which would otherwise become so long that they could not feed at all . . . On steep chalk slopes the scratching of the rabbits around their burrows, completely destroying the herbage, exposed the soil to erosion and rain-wash down the slope . . .

On the other hand, as the eminently practical Gilbert White observed: 'Rabbits make incomparably the finest turf, for they allow no bents to arise; hence warrens produce much of the most delicate turf for gardens. Sheep never touch the stalks of grass.' Thus, on those parts of the downs where rabbits were not excessively numerous the characteristic crisp springy turf, composed of dwarf plants, was the product of combined grazing by rabbits and sheep; whereas under sheep only, the herbage is not shaved so closely and the turf loses its resilience, while in the absence of intensive grazing it reverts to scrub. As we have seen, the early Neolithic farmers settled on the less heavily wooded chalk hills, and the grazing of sheep on the downs increased during the Iron

Age. Later, cattle were fattened on the gentler slopes, and the downs were subsequently colonised by rabbits, while hares and voles played minor roles in the grazing pattern.

In the 1880s Richard Jefferies could write:

> The sward is the original sward, untouched, unploughed, centuries old. It is that which was formed when the woods that covered the hills were cleared . . . The plough has nibbled at it and gnawed away great slices, but it extends mile after mile; these are mere notches on its breadth. It is as wild as wild can be without deer or savage beasts. The bees like it, and the finches come. It is silent and peaceful like the sky above.

But in the course of time all the flatter areas of the downs were cultivated, afforested, quarried or built over, with the result that by the beginning of this century the typical downland turf of dwarf herbs and grasses was restricted to the uplands. Major changes in agricultural practice, during the war years and those that followed, accelerated the break-up of the permanent pastures. Many were ploughed up, except where gradients were too steep, while the vegetational complex of the latter was altered by chemical eradication of the natural herbs and the spraying on of new seed. In the meantime, as J. D. F. Frazer has pointed out in *Animals*, the grazing of sheep on the downs had decreased with the decline of traditional shepherding practices and with the reluctance of many farmers to fence their flocks and pipe water to the uplands; and by 1946 only one flock of sheep remained in the Isle of Wight.

Finally, in the 1950s, the downland population of rabbits was decimated by the appalling myxoma virus. Probably carried accidentally to Kent in 1953 from a locality near Paris, to which it had been deliberately introduced by a Dr Armande Delille in order to exterminate the rabbits on his small estate, the virus eventually accounted for 99 per cent of those in Britain, wiping out entire local populations. So rapidly and universally did the virus spread that within one year of the initial outbreak in Kent every county except Selkirk had been affected. Yet an attempt in the 1930s to infect rabbits on the Welsh island of Skokholm with the virus had failed because there were no rabbit fleas to act as vectors, though the neighbouring island of Skomer swarmed with them; and only a year or two before its appearance in the Kent warrens some zoologists had asserted that myxomatosis would not prove effective in the British Isles, despite being 100 per cent so in controlled warrens, because wild rabbits when smitten tended to lie out in the open. There they would die or be picked up by predators before other members of the colony could be infected.

Though stocks have now built up again in many districts to numbers near the original, the rabbits' habits have changed to some extent. Because so few were left to keep open the old deep-burrow systems these collapsed, and rabbits now spend more time above ground and live in shallow burrows until or if the colony has become large enough again to excavate and maintain deep burrows. In the latter, however, the rabbit flea thrives and the colony becomes re-infected with the myxoma virus.

The Wider Effects of Myxomatosis

The reduction in the downland population of rabbits produced an immediate impact on the vegetation. This was not at first obvious everywhere because, as Frazer has emphasised, what remains of the pristine turf is restricted to the steeper slopes where there may only be a few inches of soil above the solid chalk, and this factor tends to keep the sward short, whether grazed or not; but in many places the lowering of the grazing pressure resulted in what Tansley has described as spectacular displays of spring flowers and downland orchids, offset however by a rapid invasion of coarse grasses, producing a denser, taller turf, and a scrub of bramble, gorse and hawthorn, and subsequently ash and oak seedlings.

This alteration in the downs' ancient vegetational complex has resulted in some of the typical inhabitants of a chalk grassland community becoming scarce or even extinct. The effects of myxomatosis, coupled with those of ploughing and afforestation, has for example reduced the downland population of wheatears, which require barish ground in which they can nest in holes or burrows or under stones, and on which they can pick up insects and small molluscs. These factors have also altered the ecology of the Breckland heaths, with nightjars abandoning many former nesting sites after the vegetation had grown too rank and high as a result of the extermination of the bulk of the rabbits, while stone curlews were only able to nest on tracts especially ploughed for them and on those areas of grassland maintained in a suitable condition by large numbers of sheep; but the extensive afforestation of the Brecks has not, as feared, expelled the stone curlew, since some nest freely in the forest rides and clearings, and more on reclaimed farmland.

The insect population of the Downs has also been affected by their transformation. In their original state the Downs had been gay with butterflies – adonis, chalk-hill and common blues, brown arguses, meadow browns, walls, small heaths, silver-spotted skippers. Adonis and chalk-hill blues are confined to chalk and limestone regions, because these are the habitats not only of their food plant, the horseshoe vetch, but also of certain species of red ants which milk the larvae and carry them to and place them on their correct plant near their nests. So dependent indeed on ants are the caterpillars of some butterflies that those of the large blue actually winter in ants' nests in the wild thyme and feed on the young larvae, while those of the brown argus do not thrive in captivity without ants. In a study of one area of the North Downs where, because only a few rabbits grazed it, the

7. Adonis Blues Drinking

grasses were growing taller and the scrub closing in, the number of chalk-hill blues declined from some 55,000 in 1958 to less than 200 in 1962, those of the adonis from about 4,000 to nil, and those of the meadow brown – possibly the commonest British butterfly – from 7,500 in 1957 to 2,600 in 1962. Because there did not appear to be any critical shortage of food-plants in the study area Frazer has suggested that the invasion by scrub and coarse long grasses was responsible for these dramatic decreases, possibly because once the longer grasses developed, they were colonised by voles. The extensive runways of the voles would then be used by shrews, which are avid feeders on insect larvae and pupae and could certainly have decimated both species of blues. Those meadow brown caterpillars resting high upon the grass stems would be exposed to a massive degree of parasitisation, and those lower down to shrews, though isolated populations of meadow browns can in fact decrease or increase significantly from one year to the next for no obvious reason.

The large blue is not an inhabitant of the Downs, but recent research by the Terrestrial Ecology Unit of the Nature Conservancy indicates that this butterfly's decline in its British haunts – the Cotswolds, Dartmoor and the cliffs of Cornwall and north Devon – is also mainly due to the effects of myxomatosis. Its host, the small brown ant *Myrmica sabuleti*, can only exist on arid slopes where the grass is kept shorter than three centimetres by rabbits. If, in the absence of rabbits, the grass grows higher *sabuleti* is replaced by two other species of brown ants, one of which never acts as host and the other only occasionally. But, as the editor of *Oryx* has asked, in commenting on this fascinating piece of research, what was the agent that maintained the grass at the required height for all these butterflies in prehistoric days before the introduction of sheep and rabbits? He tentatively suggests deer.

If the butterfly population of the chalk Downs fluctuates according to the level of combined grazing by sheep and rabbits, a good case has been put forward in *Animals* by J. I. Menzies for the probability that sheep-grazing on the Romney and Wallend Marshes of south-east England was responsible for their successful colonisation by the introduced marsh frog, for a batch of twelve of the latter, which included only two females, imported from Hungary in the winter of 1934-5, have now multiplied to tens of thousands. They have not, however, dispersed beyond this centre – the most northerly of their European range – which evidently holds some special attraction. In Menzies' opinion, their continued existence in this locality probably depends on the maintenance of sheep-farming in the marshes. According to him the sheep, by grazing down the vegetation on the banks of the ditches and also preventing the water in these from being invaded by a dense growth of rushes, provide conditions that appear to suit the frogs much better than those where overgrown ditches run through arable land. At present the sheep-farmers keep the ditches in good order, because maintaining them is much cheaper than fencing for separating the various flocks; but if corn and potatoes were to take the place of sheep most of the ditches would be filled in and replaced by underground drainage, except for a few large channels. In those circumstances not only the frogs, but moorhens, dabchicks, reed and sedge warblers, water voles and numerous insects would be banished.

Whether the introduction of the marsh frogs has been responsible for the total disappearance of the indigenous common frogs from the marshes, of which they previously inhabited every part, is another matter. Possibly not, for we know that the latter were already becoming uncommon in some localities – in the vicinity of Cambridge, for example – as early as the end of the nineteenth century because of the demand for specimens for laboratory dissection; and this ever-accelerating demand has certainly been a major factor contributing to the scarcity of both frogs and toads in many parts of Britain today. Since there does not appear to be any existing account of the relations between the two species of frogs, we can only note that the marsh frogs are much larger and very rarely venture far from water, and that the males are extremely pugnacious, claiming separate territories from which they vigorously repel other males: whereas common frogs and toads assemble in large numbers at their breeding pools. Although the adults of the two frogs would probably not have come into direct contact, and conflict, for the common would have finished breeding and have left the spawning pools before the marsh frogs emerged from hibernation, the former's tadpoles would have proved easy prey for the later marsh frogs.

Because the marsh frogs have inhabited their English locality for little more than forty years it is too early to claim that they are permanently established, bearing in mind the curious history of the edible frogs. It is possible that the latter may, like the European pond tortoise, have been natives of Britain during the favourable climatic conditions of the Bronze Age, and may have been indigenous in the Fens, for Thomas Bell, who was born about 1792, states that his father 'has often described to me, as long ago as I can recollect, the peculiarly loud, and somewhat musical sound uttered by the frogs of Whaddon and Foulmire [Fowlmere], which procured for them the name of "Whaddon organs".' There must therefore have been edible frogs in Cambridgeshire at least as early as the 1770s, long before the spate of importations from France and other parts of the Continent to Britain, which

8. A Natterjack Toad

included 1,500 reared in Norfolk during the years 1837-42. Moreover, the fact that they were also known, because of their vocal talents, as Cambridgeshire or Dutch nightingales and Boston waites, suggests a long local familiarity with them, though no specimen was officially recorded until 1843 – from Fowlmere. Four years later Fowlmere was drained, and that event may have terminated the edible frogs' period as 'indigenous' amphibians. Since 1837, however, several thousand have been intermittently introduced to Britain, and today there are colonies in at least eight localities in three different counties; but though some colonies may have survived for possibly more than a century, none became permanently established, unless we consider three small colonies in the general area of Fowlmere to be descendants of the pre-1847 stock.

The vocal utterances of frogs and toads evidently made a strong impression on country folk, for the distinctive and penetrating call of the natterjack toad, running over the coastal dunes and sandy inland heaths of north-west England, led to its being known as the 'Thurseley Thrush' and 'Birkdale Nightingale'. The catastrophic decline in the number of natterjacks and the contraction of their range in Britain is due entirely to man's encroachment on and destruction of their habitat. During the past thirty years they have become extinct in south-west England and Wales, and probably in the south-east too, while only four small colonies remain in East Anglia and a vestigial colony in north-east England, and they have also decreased in their Irish locality of Kerry. Today, they are mainly restricted to Lancashire and the Solway, though their 1930s population of several hundred thousand in the Lancashire dunes has been decimated by loss of habitat due to urban development and by the drying-out of the fresh-water pools or slacks in which they bred, consequent upon the general lowering of the water-table.

14 Island Ecology: Seals, Rabbits, Puffins

Seals eat the sawmon
  An' gulls eat the troots,
An' man he eats them a',
  Yet there's plenty hereaboots.
Otters eat the big fish,
  Big fish eat thc sma'
Nane'll spare the ither,
  Yet there's plenty left for a'.

We know that Mesolithic men hunted seals, for the mounds of discarded shellfish, dating from about 8000 BP, on Isle Oronsay west of Jura include the remains of both grey and common seals, whose flesh no doubt provided them with meat, as their skins did clothes and thongs.

9. Grey Seals

In Columba's time, early in the sixth century, the monks of Iona conserved the breeding stock of grey seals on a nearby rock as a source of food and light during the winter; but down the centuries the Atlantic grey seals – which were confused with the bearded seals of the Arctic until 1825 – have been ruthlessly persecuted by hunters and fishermen, particularly in Orkney and Shetland, while as long ago as the twelfth century a charter was drawn up to regulate the killing of seals by the fishermen of Bamburgh off the Farne Islands. However the slaughter by the Border fishermen, especially those engaged in salmon-fishing, continued, and the Farnes' tenants, coveting the blubber and skins, took their toll of those seals breeding in the Islands, killing as many as 72 pups in 1772. According to the state of the sea and the height of the tide, so the number of small islands and reefs of which the Farnes are composed varies from 15 to 28 exposed above water. With the most landward only 1½ miles off the mainland and six miles from Holy Island, they are therefore of relatively easy access by boat in moderate weather.

It is still difficult to assess the exact quantities of the various kinds of fish eaten by grey seals, and to determine whether or not they compete significantly with fishermen. On the one hand they take conger-eels – which prey on commercial fish – and such non-commercial species as wrasse, rays and lumpsuckers; but they also take whiting

30. A Common o
Harbour Seal

and herring and such rock and bottom fish as saithe, pollack, lythe and skate, together with cephalopods and some crustaceans. They also catch a proportion of the salmon running up rivers on the east of Scotland and the west of Ireland, and damage nets; but so far as the fishing industry is concerned, perhaps the most unacceptable fact about seals is that they carry the cod-worm parasite which, while it is not harmful to man, renders affected fish unsuitable for open sale. One should add that little is known either about the food preferences of the smaller common seals, though their diet is also very varied and includes whiting, flatties and gobies, prawns and shrimps, and particularly such shellfish as cockles and whelks.

By 1914 the grey seals were believed by some naturalists to be in danger of extinction, though this was almost certainly not the case. However, with the decline in seal-hunting during the past few decades there has been an enormous increase in the numbers of Britain's grey seals, which now constitute more than 60 per cent of the world population, though not apparently of those of the common seals, which are perhaps about a quarter as numerous. Thus in Orkney, where grey seals were comparatively rare fifty years ago, they now number more than 12,000, while on the Farnes, where the breeding stock probably never exceeded the few hundred present at the beginning of this century, but where they have enjoyed varying degrees of protection since 1920, the rookery almost doubled in size between 1940 and 1950, and has subsequently increased at the rate of 7 per cent per annum to a strength of some 6,000, making it the third largest 'closed community' in Britain, exceeded only by those in Orkney and on North Rona (8,000 - 9,000). The general increase in local populations all round the British Isles, which include 21,000 in various parts of the Hebrides, 3,000 in Shetland and possible 5,000 in south-west England and Ireland – there may also be 4,000 in the Faeroes and Iceland and about 2,000 on the Norwegian coast – has been associated with the establishment of historically new rookeries at such sites as the Isle of May and, most surprisingly, the sandy banks of Scroby Sands: a typical common seal habitat off Great Yarmouth. Population pressures in established rookeries must have been strong to cause this hiving off, for grey seals are extremely conservative in their choice of rookeries, continuing to inhabit them until long after their numbers appear to have reached a level where ground space is insufficient to allow pups to be reared without interference from neighbouring cows. Thus although the four Farne islands on which the seals breed are now becoming overcrowded, leading to aggression among the cows, the latter show little inclination to establish new colonies on unoccupied islands, though some of these Farne seals are likely to have been responsible for the new rookeries on the Isle of May and Scroby Sands. In the past they have indeed only colonised new sites at long intervals. There is no reference to their presence on North Rona, for instance, until nearly forty years after that island had become uninhabited about 1884, nor on St Kilda until after the 1930 evacuation, though a hundred pups are now born annually on Hirta.

Since the bulls haul out at the rookeries in order to establish territories in which to mate (after the cows have pupped), and since the cows, outnumbering the bulls by five or ten fold, haul out primarily to pup and only secondarily to mate, and pup whether bulls are present or not, it is reasonable to assume that it is the cows who select rookery sites in the first place and are therefore responsible for any extension of their boundaries or for establishing rookeries in new locations. Cows, incidentally, can live for more than forty years: whereas bulls apparently seldom live longer than twenty, and more normally fifteen years.

While the Baltic population of grey seals, numbering possibly 5,000, scatter to breed in small units over the ice, and those (possibly 15,000) in the Canadian maritime provinces on snow-covered islands, those in Britain tend to assemble in large rookeries on rocky islands washed by strong seas, but in caves and coves in the South-West and in Shetland. The common seals, on the other hand, breed up sea-lochs on the west coast but on mud and sand flats on the east coast, and are fairly generally distributed around the British Isles except where there are extensive cliffs. In 1703 Martin Martin stated that at the beginning of October on Eoss-uil, a small island off North Uist: 'The seals bring forth their young on the Ocean side; but those on the East side, who are of the lesser stature, bring forth their Young in the middle of June.' Although, outside the breeding season, both grey and common species may haul out at the same time this is, I believe, the only record of both breeding in one place. The islands and coves favoured by the breeding grey seals hold some special attraction for the cows not apparent to the human eye, for at other seasons they haul out on other islands and beaches which appear to be no less suitable for breeding. Different hauling-out places are also used during the moult, when the seals may assemble in herds of several thousand. These are usually sexually discrete, since the cows moult from January to March and the bulls from March to May, because the latter, after leaving the rookeries, take time off to feed up after their two months' fast before undergoing another period of intermittent starvation during the moult.

A rookery must not only be accessible from the sea, but sheltered from gales if the pups are not to be swept away in storms, for in all parts of their range the latter are born during the stormiest months of the year, though the actual pupping season varies from September on the south-west and west coasts – a small number are born late in March in Wales – to September and October on Rona, and from the latter half of October to mid-December on the Farnes. By contrast most common seal pups are born on extensive sandbanks during the relatively calm months of June and July, and, apart from man, have only to fear strong-running tides or heavy ground-swell, which may sweep them away during their mothers' absence, though it is true that they are partly seaworthy within a few hours of birth and can suckle in the sea.

Grey seals breed both on the beaches and in the interiors of islands, though the latter are not usually occupied until after shoreward zones have become congested. The Farne Islands are, for example, low-lying and provided with a minimum of one or two shelving rocky beaches, so that access to their interiors is easy and sheltered within the archipelago. Rona, on the other hand, is cliff-bound and the colossal Atlantic swell renders the sea's edge a dangerous place, even for seals; but a flattish expanse of rock at the island's northern end is sufficiently broken up for those cows hauling out to obtain a hold even when huge swells are running over it, and not to be sucked off in the backwash. Moreover, these rocks afford access by way of gullies to a broad peninsula, and thence up to a moor 300 or 400 yards from the sea and as high as 300 feet above it.

At first sight a high island such as Rona would appear to be a much safer habitat for the pups than ledges in the deep recesses of caves or small coves or narrow strips of pebble beaches backed by cliffs, all of which are overrun by big seas pounding on the shore and flooding into caves at spring-tides; and more suitable than the flattish island rocks of the Farnes over which the seas break in force 10 gales. Pups born in such situations, at or only a little above sea-level, are constantly threatened by rough seas, for though they can swim in still rock pools when only two or three days old, they are not seaworthy for several days or weeks after birth. Such seas wash them out of caves and suck them off the beaches, or wedge them into crevices from which they cannot subsequently extricate themselves, batter them to death on the rocks, carry them away into the breakers.

Nevertheless, the mortality among the pups is no less on Rona than it is at those breeding stations swept by storms, for pups born in large overcrowded colonies are exposed to dangers not experienced by those in small colonies. On Rona, where more than 2,000 pups occupy only one-third of the 300 acres of moor available, many are born and crushed in the traffic lane of bulls continually coming and going from the sea; while cows breeding in crowded conditions are liable to be aggressive towards each other and also to pups of other cows straying near them. In these circumstances frightened pups become isolated from their mothers, wander about the rookery and, soliciting other cows, are snapped at or actually bitten, or fall into trenches or crevices. Moreover those cows breeding furthest from the sea, and having to pass through the ranks of other aggressive cows, may not be able to suckle their pups often enough during the critical first two days.

The congested state of the rookery on the Farne Islands now poses a serious ecological problem affecting the well-being of their other inhabitants, and one solution, culling large numbers of the seals at intervals, has proved controversial; for the dramatic increase in the tonnage of seals is resulting in a drastic erosion of the thin layer of soil covering these rocky islands, thereby putting at risk the continued existence of such burrow-nesting birds as puffins. The numbers of the latter are already declining catastrophically on other British islands from causes not fully established, though rats, gulls and oil pollution have certainly contributed to this decline. On two of the Farne islands (connected at low water) on which puffins nest and on which are the largest rookeries of seals, there has also existed for an unknown number of years a small but unique population of reddish or ginger-coloured rabbits. A warden on the Farnes, John Cranham, was inspired to undertake a two-year study of these rabbits, with most enlightening results, for if ever there was an example of the survival of the fittest, it is that of this island population of rabbits. From the time of their first litters of young, early in April, the rabbits are engaged in a ceaseless struggle to survive, since the birth of the earliest litters coincides with the return of the puffins to nest and of severe competition for burrows between them and the rabbits. In Cranham's experience the puffins are the victors more often than not, with the result that the majority of the rabbits are allowed to occupy only those burrows surplus to the puffins' requirements. The question is, then, will the seals' erosion of the islands' crust benefit the rabbits by rendering it unsuitable for the puffins, or also make it untenable for the rabbits?

The return of the puffins is, however, only the beginning of the rabbits' trials, for no sooner have the young been born than the does, now obliged to spend much of their time feeding above ground, are exposed to continuous attacks by the sharp-beaked terns on whose nesting grounds they encroach. Later, herring gulls and lesser black-backs take their toll of the young rabbits when they are old enough to venture out of their burrows. Furthermore, by July the luxuriant spring herbage, including the rabbits' favourite chickweed, is withering on the thin porous soil, and by September the only remaining green vegetation is the sea-campion, which cannot be classed as normal rabbit food. Finally, from late October until the close of the year the thousands of seals are churning the herbage floor into a morass, and gales and drenching sea-spray complete the devastation. How, then, are the rabbits to avoid starvation during the winter and early spring? A very limited supply of food can no doubt be obtained from plant roots, but Cranham observed that during the spells of fair weather in winter the rabbits were to be found, day and night, feeding on seaweed, whether growing on the rocks or washed up by storms. Seaweed has of course some nutritional value, and the channelled-wrack's mat of short multi-branched fronds, which grows in a narrow band near and just below the high-water line, serves as a subsistence fare for ponies, cattle and sheep along many stretches of coast in the Highlands and Hebrides and in Shetland.

In addition to seaweed the Farne rabbits nibbled at the lichen on the rocks and gnawed at driftwood, providing that this had not been tarred or creosoted. Against all odds, therefore, the Farne community has been able to survive primarily by beachcombing during the winter –

1. Guillemot Rock in the Farne Islands

but only just, for by the end of the winter the summer population of eighty may have been reduced to fewer than ten, while the average doe has produced only nine young with the completion of her final litter early in July.

From an ecological viewpoint even more interesting than the rabbits' survival is Cranham's argument that they present a perfect example of natural population control, and that any attempt to improve their status would be disastrous not only for them but also for other inhabitants of the islands. He maintains that any artificial enrichment of the vegetation would inevitably result in the numbers of rabbits increasing during the summer to such an extent that the bare minimum of food available during the winter would be over-exploited, with the result that the entire community might starve. If, on the other hand, the rabbits were removed from the Farnes, the herbage complex might be radically changed. An experiment on the Inner Farne, the largest of the islands, supports this possibility. In the autumn of 1968 the feral grey and black-and-white descendants of stock introduced by generations of lighthouse keepers were exterminated, and during the next two years Cranham observed that initially the various flowering plants, and in particular thrift, grew more profusely than previously, while clover and dandelions reappeared; but in the third year docks, nettles and such coarse grasses as Yorkshire fog rampaged, crowding out many of the weaker but more valuable plants. As a result of this change in the vegetational pattern, and also because of the density of the new growth, the three species of terns – common, arctic and roseate – which habitually nested on the rabbit-controlled swards, were unable to continue doing so; and their colonies were further reduced by the heavy mortality among the chicks, which, unable to escape out of the jungle of thick wet grass during rainy periods, died from exposure. In place of rabbits, chemical sprays and motor-mowers are now required to control the herbage in the tern colonies!

By contrast we might cite the situation on St Kilda, where, since the evacuation of the human population, their sheep stock has bred and grazed uncontrolled, with the result that the herbage on the three main islands now consists of a fine short greensward. But the consequence of this has been that such burrow-nesting birds as puffins and shearwaters are now being restricted to steep cliff-slopes and the lesser islets because the adults returning to their nesting burrows, and the young leaving them, have been deprived of long cover in which to conceal themselves from the increasing population of large predatory gulls.

15 Sharp-Eyed Opportunists

Various corvines, thrushes, finches, tits and creepers, shrikes, woodpeckers, pigeons, raptors and owls, together with woodcock and grouse, may all have inhabited Britain during the inter-glacial periods of the Pleistocene, though banished to more southerly and easterly regions with renewed glaciation. When the ice-sheet finally receded northwards and was replaced by tundra, its scrubby birchwoods must have been colonised by such species as redpolls, willow warblers, fieldfares and redwings. Presumably bramblings would also have bred in the tundra birchwoods, but though a pair apparently laid seven eggs in a Sutherland nest in 1920 some factor has normally prevented these finches from breeding in Britain within ornithological history. That factor is probably the lack of suitable habitats, for in Europe they are most numerous near the limit of tree growth in high latitudes or at high altitudes, and nest mainly in sub-arctic birchwoods, though also in open conifer forest and tall willow scrub. In late springs, however, large numbers of bramblings cut short their northward return from their winter quarters and nest further south than usual; and this departure from the norm may account for the Sutherland record.

By the Neolithic era much of Britain was a 'wild woodland of badly-grown oak forest with fern brakes and dense tangled thickets of blackthorn and bramble'; the valleys were choked with marshes, fens and backwaters, interspersed here and there with clumps of alder and willow; and vast tracts of upland moor were overgrown with heather seven feet high. Such an environment would have been favourable to bird life, but less so for small passerines, a high proportion of which characteristically restrict their territories in the forest to the less thickly wooded fringes, where the canopy thins out, allowing sunlight to reach the ground and encourage secondary growth, and where there are open spaces in which they can feed. However, as Neolithic man hacked at and burned the woods on the higher ground, so his clearings and shifting cultivation must have increased the variety of habitats and food available to increasing numbers and species of passerines. In Britain, therefore, their environment has only been influenced by man's activities during the past four or five thousand years. We know that jays, jackdaws, crows, rooks, ravens and magpies were all associated with the New Stone Age agriculture and, as E.M. Nicholson has conjectured in *Birds and Men*, such sharp-eyed opportunists as jackdaws and other crows must have been among the first birds to take advantage of man the cultivator and herdsman. For how many centuries had jackdaws nested in the interstices between the uprights and imposts of Stonehenge before Gilbert White recorded them doing so?

In his lively book, *Man and Birds*, R.K. Murton has allowed his imagination to take flight and speculate that no observer alive in Neolithic Britain could have guessed that felling woods and grazing sheep, thereby creating scrub, would create an ideal environment for a small bird that may formerly have been confined to Poland and western Russia – the dunnock. According to Murton, the dunnock has probably colonised the western Palearctic comparatively recently and is the only representative in Britain of a genus that has eleven species in the central Palearctic extending from Russian Turkestan and the Himalayas north to Siberia and east to Mongolia and Japan. All are insectivorous birds, living in the thin scrub of the forest edge, particularly in montane habitats where trees become shrubs; while many inhabit gulleys in rough and broken ground above the shrub line. Thus the alpine accentor shares its summer home of rocks, lichen and gentians at the edge of the snow with choughs and whistling marmots at altitudes of over 10,000 feet, nesting in rock crevices and feeding on insects; but descends during heavy winter snow to the foothills to feed on berries and seeds, sheltering in village barns at night and picking up crumbs from the balconies of chalets.

There are, alas, no contemporary accounts of bird life in Neolithic Britain. We may surmise that once the demands of everyday existence had eased sufficiently for men not to be engaged for every minute of their short lives in the ceaseless struggle for food, warmth and shelter, there would be a few to whom birds and beasts were not solely objects of food or skins or for the pleasure of the chase, but sources of spiritual, poetical or artistic inspiration. Such men have been found mainly among the less physically active – in later ages the monks and scholars. Upwards of thirty thousand lines of poetry, the corpus composed by the twelfth century, await exploration by some naturalist student of old English; and there must also be items of interest among the old Celtic poems. The following lines are, for example, attributed to St Columba early in the sixth century:

How happy the son of Dima of the devout church
When he hears in Durrow the desire of his mind:
The Sound of the wind against the elms when 'tis played,
The blackbird's joyous note when he claps his wings,

To listen at early dawn in Ros-grencha to the cattle,
The cooing of the cuckoo from the tree on the brink of summer.

In the next century another Irish poet paints an idyllic scene in *King and Hermit*:

I have a shieling in the wood,
None knows it save my God,
An ash-tree on the hither side, a hazel-bush beyond,
A huge old tree encompasses it.

Two heath-clad doorposts for support,
And a lintel of honeysuckle:
The forest around its narrowness sheds
Its mast upon fat swine . . .

From its gable a sweet strain sings
A she-bird in her cloak of ousel's hue . . .

Around it tame swine lie down,
Goats, pigs,
Wild swine, grazing deer,
A badger's brood . . .

Swarms of bees and chafers, the little musicians of the world,
A gentle chorus:
Wild geese and ducks, shortly before summer's end,
The music of the dark torrent.

An active songster, a lively wren
From the hazel bough,
Beautiful hooded birds, woodpeckers,
A vast multitude.

While a series of short Irish verses, which can probably be assigned to the eighth century, include:

A grove surrounds me,
The swift lay of the blackbird makes music to me.
I will not hide in it.
Over my much-lined little book
The song of the bird makes music to me.

This vivid appreciation of Nature was still apparent centuries later when John of Fornsete, a monk of Reading Abbey, composed in 1226 the earliest English song of which the music is extant:

Sumer is i-cumen in,
Lhude sing cuccu!
Groweth sed and bloweth med,
And springeth the wude nu –
Sing cuccu!

Awe bleteth after lomb,
Lhouth after calve cu;
Bulluc sterteth, bucke verteth,
Murie sing cuccu!

Cuccu, cuccu, wel sings thu cuccu,
Ne swik thu naver nu.
Sing cuccu, nu, sing cuccu,
Sing cuccu, sing cuccu, nu!

It was in that century too that one of those early monks, the admirable Matthew Paris, showed us what articulate descriptions of bird life they might have bequeathed to us. He is writing in 1251 of an irruption of crossbills:

> At the turn of the same year, at the season of fruits, certain wonderful birds never before seen in England appeared, particularly in orchards. They were a little bigger than larks and ate the pips of apples and nothing else from the apples. So they robbed the trees of their fruit very grievously. Moreover they had the parts of the beak crossed (lattice-wise) and with them split the apples as if with pincers or a pocket-knife. The pieces of the apples which they left were apparently tainted with poison.

Since that year there have been many invasions of crossbills, usually in June or July after the crop of spruce seed has failed in the forests of northern Europe, and almost invariably it is the apple trees that have brought them to the notice of those with orchards, who dubbed them the 'shell-apple'. Thus in 1602 we read that:

> In Queen Elizabeth's time there came a flocke of birds into Cornwall, about Harvest Season, in bignesse not much exceeding a sparrow, which made a foule spoyle of the apples. Their bills were thwarted crosswide at the end, and with these they would cut an apple in two at one snap, eating Onely the Kernels.

And again, in 1640:

> That the yeere 1593 was a greate and exceeding yeere of apples; and there were greate plenty of strang birds, that shewed themselves at the time the apples were full rype, who fed upon the Kernells onely of these apples, and havinge a bill with one beak wrythinge over the other, which would presently bore a greate hole in

:2. A Crossbill

the apple, and make way to the Kernells; they were of the bignesse of a bullfinch, the henne right like the henne of the Bullfinch in coulour: the cock a very glorious bird, in a manner al redde or yellowe on the brest, backe and heade. The oldest man living never heard or reade of any such bird; and the thinge most to be noted was, that it seemed they came out of some country not inhabited, for that they would at first abide shooting at them, either with pellet, bowe, or other engine, and not remove till they were stricken downe; moreover, they would abide the throweing at them . . . with apples. They came when the apples were rype, and went away when the apples were cleane fallen. They were a very good meat.

Two centuries later the Northumbrian naturalist, Prideaux John Selby, also noted that there were immense flocks of crossbills in the south of England from June 1821. Some of these invading crossbills, which are mainly immature birds, have established resident colonies in Britain, but these have usually died out after two or three generations, though one colony is still in existence in Scots pines on the Brecks, following an invasion in 1910.

16 The Invasion of the Gardens

The progressive and continuous destruction of forest in Britain from its primeval forty million acres or more to some three million acres before the last war, and some four and a half million acres today, must have resulted in a reduction in the numbers of purely woodland birds and sweeping changes in the types of habitats available. One new habitat came into existence during the latter half of the eighteenth century with the introduction to the English landscape of plantations and gardens around gentlemen's houses. These offered not only a variety of nesting niches, but also food supplied by the intensive production of vegetable matter and its attendant insects and invertebrates. The result was that such woodland birds as robins, blackbirds and song thrushes, which could take advantage of these amenities, became among the most numerous in Britain, while specialised birds such as tree-creepers discovered that they could excavate their half-egg-shaped roosting cavities in the soft, corrugated bark of the Wellingtonias – the *Sequoia gigantes* of California – thoughtfully planted by the 'Improvers' between 1835 and 1890. Although these cavities, about the size of an old penny and up to two inches deep, had been noticed in the trunks of Wellingtonias in the Highlands as early as 1905, and in England in 1910 and in Ireland in 1923, the fact that they were treecreeper roosts was not recognised until the latter year. Between 1930 and 1940, as the Wellingtonias matured, their use as roosting sites spread rapidly to nearly every county in the British Isles, perhaps because the extensive felling of old timber had resulted in a scarcity of suitable trees.

Robins

There are frequent references in Celtic poetry, whether Irish, Scottish or Welsh, to the blackbird and the cuckoo, but not to the robin, despite its uniquely confident relationship with man, though it features among the 75 species on the Saxon bird list – as do such other small passerines as chaffinch, goldfinch, dunnock, song thrush, starling, nightingale, redstart and red-backed shrike. William Turner – a native of Morpeth in

Northumberland who, however, passed much of his adult life in exile on the Continent, and who published the world's first printed book on birds, the *Avium Pracipuarum*, in 1544 – noted that in England the robin:

> Nests as far as possible from towns and cities, in the thickest briers and shrubs after this fashion. Where it finds oak leaves in plenty, or leaves like the oak, it builds its nest among the leaves themselves close to the roots of briers or the thicker shrubs: and when completed covers it with leaves as if with topiary work. Nor does access lie open to the nest on every side, but by one way alone is entrance gained. And at that place when it enters the nest the bird builds a long porch of leaves before the doorway and, on going forth to feed, closes the end with leaves.

Until the nineteenth century robins continued to be common around man's habitation only during the winter months, returning to the woods to nest. 'We scarcely recollect one of those old-fashioned sunk sawpits, built on the sides with dry stones, moss-grown with time and margined with a split log, that did not possess its robins, quietly sitting while the men wrought,' wrote Sir William Jardine in 1839. They still tend to be woodland birds in rural areas of Britain, nesting secretively in tree cavities, ivy or grassy banks, and well within the pine forests of the central Highlands though usually near paths or heather banks. But with the proliferation of gardens and subsequently of suburbia an ever-increasing proportion of robins began to become permanently resident in urban areas. On the Continent, too, they are become increasingly frequent visitors to gardens, though still particularly so after the nesting season, for there they remain a predominantly woodland species, and in the Alps both robins and dunnocks, after wintering near towns or rivers in the valleys, retreat into the forests to nest. Although these alpine robins may in fact suffer a heavy mortality during winter snowstorms in the valleys, theirs is a special case, and in general there are obvious advantages to be gained by some small passerines in changing their habitat from natural forest to artificial gardens, for a major problem of insectivorous ground feeders must be that of obtaining sufficient food during the winter. This can be solved by taking advantage of urban man's cultivation and generous scraps instead of undertaking an arduous and hazardous migration. Moreover, if a species' population is multiplying and extending its geographical range, an extra habitat increases the number of potential territories and thereby lessens the competition for them.

Tits

Other small birds that have benefited from the modern garden landscape, and especially from suburban bird-tables, are the tits. Yet all the tits are essentially woodland birds that still inhabit every wood in

Britain, including the remotest glens in the Forest of Caledon, and each species is nicely adapted to working in that type of tree in which it searches for its invertebrate food. In a study of their feeding habits Linda Partridge has suggested in *Wildlife* that the coal tit's slender beak is, for example, especially suitable for extracting the small insects living in the clusters of pine needles: whereas the blue tit's shorter, stouter beak can cope with the larger and tougher insects and their larvae inhabiting oak trees. The two species also have differently shaped feet. Those of the coal tit have relatively long toes, which may help to spread the bird's slight weight over a large area of pine needles when standing on them, whereas the blue tit has short opposable toes, enabling it to hang from the edges of the flat leaves of deciduous trees.

In the context of a suburban habitat blue tits and great tits are of particular interest because, since about 1920, they have exploited a new source of artificial food in the form of the top of the milk obtained by pecking at bottle-tops, initially waxboard and subsequently metal. During the first decade of this innovation – when isolated 'attacks' by marsh and coal tits, blackbirds, song thrushes, robins, dunnocks, chaffinches and starlings were also recorded – there were outbreaks in nine separate areas from Kent to Northern Ireland. Nevertheless, the rapid radiation of the habit around centres suggests that one tit imitated another. A parallel is to be found in the greenfinch's addiction to the red fruits of the *Daphne mezerum* shrub. This addiction apparently began in a small northern town in the 1930s, but within twenty years had spread to various parts of Britain, and by the 1960s was prevalent on the Continent. No doubt the animosity of

33. A Blue Ti
a Milk Bo

house sparrows towards crocuses and primulas followed a similar course, for Bolam did not notice this aberration in Northumberland until the early years of this century. House sparrows have also been known to peck open bottle-tops, as have pied woodpeckers and jackdaws in Copenhagen, while in Sweden, where the habit was widespread among blue and great tits in the late 1940s and early 1950s, blackbirds and magpies also took part.

That tits should exploit the possibilities of milk-bottles is not quite so remarkable as it appears superficially, since hammering at objects in order to obtain food, or while searching for food, is a natural action of theirs, particularly when they are exploring new woods during their autumnal wanderings. Eric Simms has described in *Birds of Town and Suburb* how during the large-scale autumn invasion of Britain by Continental tits in 1957 many blue and great tits entered houses and attacked wallpaper, books, newspapers, lampshades, notices and labels – one blue tit enjoyed a dust-bath in a powder-bowl on a dressing-table. Others attacked calendars, letters, printed forms, blotting-paper, toilet rolls and tissue paper, curtains, towels, bedspreads, telephone wires and candles and, outside the houses, paint, whitewash, mortar and especially putty – which starlings have been observed eating by pecking at newly glazed windows. Paper-tearing by tits is not, however, a new development, for it was referred to as long ago as 1693 in a poem on paper-making, *Papyrus*, by Father Jean Imberbis:

Small is this naughty Fowl, yet it can wreak
No small Destruction with its claws and beak.
For, when paper from afar it spies,
Straightway through open Window in it flies.
Its frequent blows the sheets do quickly tear
Still sodden, and make Havoc everywhere. . .
To Gin and Snare it grows too soon inured,
And Carelessness is by Experience cured.
The Lime untouched, always the saucy Tit,
So keen its zest, to Paper straight will flit.

Bullfinches

In the sixteenth century a reward was paid for 'everie Bulfynche or other Byrde that devoureth the blowthe of fruit', and in 1618 William Lawson lamented in his *New Orchard and Garden* that 'The Bull-finch is a devourer of your fruit in the budde. I have had whole trees shalde out with them in Winter time . . . Your cherries when they bee ripe, will draw all the blackebirds, Thrushes and May-pyes to your Orchard.' Nevertheless, bullfinches in general appear to have been late in taking advantage of the new man-made environment, for it was only in the 1950s that there was a notable increase in their numbers throughout the British Isles. This was particularly marked in Ireland and Scotland,

and was associated with a dispersal from their natural haunts of woodland and scrub into agricultural land, towns, parks and some parts of suburbia. Bullfinches have a curious habitat distribution. Throughout most of Europe and western Siberia they live in coniferous forest, providing that this has a fairly dense undergrowth; but at the western and eastern extremes of their range, in Britain and Japan, they are essentially inhabitants of deciduous woodlands, though in the central Highlands of Scotland they do not in fact breed in the birch and alder woods, but nest mainly in the old pine forest or in mixed woods where pines or spruce predominate. They are indeed to be found in the pinewoods of Glen Feshie, Rothiemurchus, Glen More and Abernethy almost up to the 2,000 feet contour in the high glens of the Forest of Caledon.

In their original British habitat the bullfinches fed mainly on the buds of conifers, birch and willow; but with their invasion of deciduous lowland woods – in which their main food in spring comprised the buds of crab-apple and hawthorn – and their colonisation of rural areas they have become a major pest in orchards. Since their increase might be attributed to the overkill of such natural bullfinch controllers as jays, magpies, crows, stoats and weasels, fruit-growers are perhaps paying the penalty for the excesses of game preservers. According to Simms those trees at the edge of an orchard and nearest to woodland or scrub are attacked first and systematically stripped of their buds, as the birds alight near the tip of a branch and remove every bud in turn while making their way towards the bole of the tree. However, although a bullfinch can nip off thirty or more buds a minute, research suggests that half the buds on a pear tree could be removed without in fact diminishing the ultimate crop of fruit. It must also be emphasised that orchards are usually only liable to attack every second year when the local crop of ash seed-keys is poor, and that for two-thirds of the year bullfinches feed on the seeds of such weeds as sorrel, thistle, nettle, groundsel, dandelion, dock and plantain, and on the larvae of such injurious insects as the winter moths that ravage orchards, and also feed their nestlings on seeds and larvae.

Blackbirds

In all cases – whether the colonisers were bullfinches, robins, tits, dunnocks, song thrushes or blackbirds – the invasion of gardens, suburbs and towns began earlier in Britain than on the Continent. All northern thrushes except the ring ousel have now become adapted to urban habitats, and since early in the nineteenth century even so shy and wild a bird as the mistle thrush has spread spectacularly, not only over Ireland and north Britain but also over west and central Europe, colonising plantations, coniferous woods, parks, gardens and city centres. However, the most universal of these dispersals has been that of the blackbird. It is difficult to assess the earlier status of blackbirds in Britain. Robert Spencer has conjectured in his book *The*

Blackbird that when much of Britain was still under forest blackbirds must have been almost exclusively woodland dwellers, feeding on insects and worms from the forest floor and on wild cherries, crab apples and berries when these ripened. In winter, when human activity broke up the carpet of snow, giving access to the ground beneath, they would have ventured into hamlets and villages. From the poems quoted in the previous chapter it is evident that in Ireland at any rate the songs of blackbirds in their territories were very familiar to the early clerics: yet by the late eighteenth and early nineteenth centuries the blackbird of the ornithologists – Montagu, Bewick, Selby – was at all seasons a wild, shy solitary species frequenting woods and thickets. As one account in 1794 states: 'The ouzel is a solitary bird . . . He inhabits solitary and rocky woods near rivulets, and when surprised in his lonely haunts, flies from the presence of the intruder with an hideous loud scream.' There are still large numbers of blackbirds in our deciduous woods and at the edges of the more open conifer forest, but with the long-term clearance of primeval forest their kind were able to adapt so successfully to a farmland habitat that today there may be more blackbirds per acre than in most other types of country.

It was not until the 1830s that there were reports of blackbirds wintering in gardens and near towns, and the end of that century before they were being recorded as permanently resident in suburbia, whose gardens, with their trees, bushes and creepers, were fair substitutes for woodlands and were rendered more attractive by the provision of water and scraps in winter. During the 1920s and 1930s blackbirds colonised most large towns in Britain, and by the mid-1930s had moved into central London. Today they are, after house sparrows, the dominant species in some suburban areas, despite the fact that domestic cats are as deadly as wild cats and martens, and their density in London is much greater than in rural areas, with a typically high incidence of partial albinism. Some indeed – as Simms has pointed out – may be watched defending territories among the roofs of city buildings, and there is hardly a town park anywhere in Britain that does not have its resident pair of blackbirds, which are now probably the most numerous of British breeding passerines.

The inward spread of blackbirds from country to town in Britain has obviously been coincident not only with a substantial increase in their numbers but with an expansion of their geographical range: Shetland, for example, was not colonised until the 1870s. This has also been the case on a much greater scale in Europe, and has been associated with a general rise in temperatures over northern Europe, which might be regarded as a further retreat of the Ice Age. The Faeroes were colonised in 1947 and a thriving community established, and more recently Iceland. There have also been considerable extensions of range northwards in Finland not only of blackbirds – which first bred in the extreme south-west of that country at the end of the nineteenth century, and by the 1950s were nesting as far north as the head of the

Gulf of Bothnia – but of starlings, jackdaws, blue tits and ringdoves. And just as the shift of robins and blackbirds from a rural to an urban habitat is initiated by their appearance in gardens as winter visitors, and only subsequently as permanent residents, so in northern Europe several years or even decades may elapse between the arrival of a new species as a winter visitor and its ultimate establishment as a breeding species. So, too, the blackbirds' dispersal over Europe has been linked with their invasion of towns, which was first noted in Holland about 1820, in Denmark about 1890, in Sweden about 1900, Finland about 1924 and Königsberg (Kalinigrad) about 1933. Since then they have occupied more and more European towns and villages, and their numbers have greatly increased. In Europe, as in Britain, their density is now higher in gardens and parks than in rural areas; and still their dispersal continues, for only now are they penetrating the towns of eastern Europe in the course of their advance eastwards.

Afforestation

However in Britain we are now witnessing a new phase in the distribution of birds, for, as W.B. Yapp has pointed out in *Birds and Woods*, the vast afforestation with conifers undertaken by the Forestry Commission during the past sixty years, and in particular the planting of spruce on a large scale, with the consequent raising of the altitudinal limit for seedling trees, is taking some species of woodland birds out again to localities they had abandoned when the forests were replaced by sheep-walks. Between 1950 and 1960, for example, lesser redpolls began nesting in young conifers from six to twenty feet high, and spread over most of Britain and also along the sandy coastline of Denmark and Holland. It is possible that the Commission's plantations may prove to be as influential in redistributing our woodland birds as were the Enclosures and subsequently the gardens of suburbia; but it must not be forgotten that while plantations of young conifers attract such birds as redpolls, grasshopper warblers, short-eared owls and hen-harriers, and older plantations coal tits and crossbills, other existing species are lost when oak woods, which are the preferred habitat of many birds, are felled to make way for introduced species of conifers.

In Scotland the dramatic increase in such woodland species as mistle thrushes, bullfinches, redpolls, goldcrests, stockdoves and woodcock can be attributed to the extensive planting in the eighteenth and nineteenth centuries; and the enormous build-up of wood pigeons was due in large degree to the expansion of conifer plantations, though also to the cultivation of winter roots and clover and to the extermination of predatory hawks and egg-eating crows and magpies in game preserves. Prior to replanting, deforestation in the Highlands and more particularly the destruction of old timber, which offered both nesting facilities and food in the form of wood-boring grubs, had resulted in the pied woodpecker becoming extremely scarce by the middle of the nine-

34. A Pied Woodpecker

teenth century. But substantial tracts of pine forest survived in Strathspey, and since pairs of woodpeckers were reported there in the 1880s, only thirty years after their reputed extinction, there is no reason why some should not have survived in that locality. They were certainly present there up to the time that the Improvers' plantings matured, and these would have provided an additional habitat. At all events, northern England and southern Scotland were recolonised before the end of the nineteenth century, and woodpeckers are now once again back in Sutherland, from which they had disappeared about 1850.

Deforestation

Deforestation may, however, have resulted in the extinction of the capercaillie, and also in a contraction of the range of crested tits and the native crossbills; and the dearth of woods modified the nesting habits of herons, many of which took to nesting on cliffs, while rooks and wood pigeons were obliged to nest in the heather, as the latter still do in Orkney. Some ornithologists believe that the last indigenous capercaillie in Scotland were shot near Balmoral in 1785 – soon after they had been finally exterminated in Ireland – and that early nineteenth-century records were those of unsuccessful re-introductions,

35. A Capercaillie

as was the case at Mar Lodge in 1827 and 1831; but other ornithologists think that some of the native stock may in fact have survived, since there was an interval of only about twenty years between possible sightings on west Inverness-shire and Argyll, and the successful introduction in 1837 of 50 or 60 Swedish caper at Taymouth Castle in Perthshire. At any rate, after a further shipment from Sweden the following year and at least 25 subsequent importations, the caper spread rapidly over the central and northern Highlands, and as far south as Forth and Clyde. They colonised plantations of young pines fifteen to twenty years old and especially the native pine forest, with its well-spaced trees and bushy clearings of heather, blaeberry and juniper thickets, wherein they could feed almost exclusively on the needles and shoots of the pines during the winter, supplemented at other seasons by insects and such fruits as blaeberry.

17 The Scavengers

> We stryve as did the houndes for the boon.
> They foughte al day, and yet hir part was noon;
> Ther cam a kyte, whyl that they were wrothe, And
> bar away the boon betwixte hem bothe.
>
> *The Knight's Tale*, 1387

Ravens and Crows

In the excavations at Roman Silchester the bones of ravens and, to a lesser extent, of crows were only less numerous than those of barnyard fowls. Both ravens and crows were very common in English towns from Roman times until the Restoration, and were more or less protected because they performed the essential urban scavenging role for the ever-dirty townsmen that vultures still perform in Africa and the East. In a letter home during the winter of 1496-7 the Venetian ambassador observed –

> Nor do they dislike what we so much abominate, i.e. crows, rooks, and jackdaws; and the raven may croak at his pleasure, for no one cares for the omen; there is even a penalty attached to destroying them, as they say they keep the streets of the town free from all filth. It is the same with the kites, which are so tame, that they often take out of the hands of little children, the bread smeared with butter . . . given to them by their mothers –

while a German traveller, Von Wedel, describing a journey through north Britain in September 1584, wrote:

> On the 6th we rode to Belfart [Belford], twelve miles, and from thence twelve miles again with fresh post to Barwick [Berwick] . . . The homes in this town are mean and thatched with straw . . .

> There are many ravens in this town which it is forbidden to shoot, upon pain of a crown's payment, for they are considered to drive away bad air.

William Harrison noted that:

> I have seen the carren crows so cunning also by their own industry of late, that they have used to soar over great rivers (as the Thames for example) and, suddenly coming down, have caught a small fish in their feet and gone away withal without wetting of their wings.

On this observation one can comment that crows do in fact occasionally pick up dead fish from the water, though usually with their beaks; while both crows and ravens occasionally carry food with their feet.

Kites

Kites are mentioned in the *Anglo-Saxon Chronicle*, and every visitor to Britain was astonished at their numbers in our towns. The Bohemian Schaschek stated in his *Diary* for 1465-7 that nowhere had he seen so many kites as in the vicinity of London Bridge, while the following century the Flemish naturalist Charles Lécluse considered the red kites to be as numerous in London as the black kites in Cairo, and therefore to be numbered in thousands rather than in hundreds. He added that they ate the refuse in the gutters and ventured into the butchers' booths to filch meat. Their boldness was proverbial. As early as the second century AD kites in Britain had been credited with plucking

36. A Red Kite

hair from people's heads for nesting material, and William Turner confirmed the tameness of the London kites, observing that:

> He is bold some tyme in England (I never saw it so nether in Italy nether in any parte of Germany where as I have bene) that he dare take butter and bread out of boys handes in the strete . . . And all the hole year thorowe there is no pray that cometh amyss unto him, he eateth al kynde of carion . . . In the tyme that he byldeth hys nest he caryeth al that he can catche and snatche unto it, ragges, cloutes, napkins, kerches, boys cappes, and some tyme purses as I have herde say.

No doubt there was competition for carrion between kites and ravens, for Sir William Browne, writing from Norwich in 1659, states: 'Ravens in good plenty about the citty wch makes so few Kites to be seen hereabouts.'

In Scotland the kites did not apparently scavenge the streets of towns, though they filched clothes off the line and paper for their nests; they also took poultry, but fed mainly on carrion. Jardine did not know any place where they were more abundant than on either side of Loch Fine, and relates how, at the Inveraray herring-curing station: 'When the curers retired to their meals six or seven of these birds would frequently sail down from the neighbouring wood and, uttering their shrill squeal, carry off the cleanings.'

Although kites were nesting with rooks and magpies in the trees around St Giles-in-the-Field in 1734, and young ones with frogs in their stomachs were taken from a nest in Gray's Inn in 1777, they had virtually ceased to breed in London by Gilbert White's day because, so it is said, improving sanitary conditions in English towns had deprived them of their living; but this explanation hardly seems to square with the fact that as late as 1840 30,000 sheep and cattle were being driven through the streets of London once a week to the slaughter-houses of Smithfield, which had no facilities for the disposal of offal. One might also add that at that time pigs were being kept in dwelling-houses in the slums, and that a dozen cartloads of horse dung were being removed from Regent Street every day.

Today the kites' role as town scavengers has been taken over by gulls, especially by herring gulls, whose numbers have multiplied in recent decades on both sides of the North Sea to such an extent that there are now estimated to be half a million pairs in Britain alone, and their population is doubling every six years. Moreover, with coastal nesting sites becoming overcrowded, particularly in north Yorkshire, Durham, Northumberland and south Wales, they have since the 1940s or 1950s begun to invade not only inland crags, mountain lakes and china-clay pits, but also towns, where they nest on the roofs of houses and factories. Since their average life-span is fifteen years, and that of individuals twice as long, their invasions of towns is beginning to pose

37. A Hen Red Kite and Her Young

problems similar to those presented by the enormous roosts of starlings.

Whatever may have been the reasons for the kites' disappearance from the towns, in rural areas their partiality for chickens and ducklings, and persecution by gamekeepers, had resulted in their extinction in half the English counties by early in the nineteenth century. During the seventeenth century indeed, churchwardens in two villages – one in Cheshire, the other in Kent – both paid out head-money for more than four hundred kites in twelve years. The last English pair nested in Lincolnshire in 1870, shortly before their extermination in all parts of Britain except Wales. Living near man they were easy to shoot, trap or poison at carrion and, once they had become rare, collectors finished them off, with the fanatically ruthless E.T. Booth, for instance, being largely responsible for the slaughter of the last red kites in the Speyside forests in the late 1870s.

The evidence of Turner and Lécluse indicates that the London kites were of the red species. There is indeed no known case of the black breeding in Britain, and they have only been sighted in this country a dozen times during the past hundred years or so, despite the fact that on the Continent they, and not the red, are the common scavengers, and are the most frequently seen birds of prey, whether scavenging for dead and dying fish along rivers and coastlines or on the wing over forest and steppe throughout Europe, with the exception of Holland and an eastern strip of Iberia.

With extraordinary tenacity a small nucleus of red kites have been able to survive throughout the twentieth century in their last sanctuary in Britain — mid-Wales. That they have been able to do so must be attributed mainly to long-term protection. There may, however, have been intermittent reinforcement from the Continent, for the poisoned one of a pair of immature kites, established in a territory in Radnor, had been ringed the previous year in Schleswig-Holstein, in the extreme north of their European range. But why should Continental kites locate the only breeding place of their kind in the British Isles? The Welsh sanctuary contains most of their requirements in a rural habitat, including oak woods that provide essential roosting and nesting sites. These, however, have now been reduced to small hanging remnants, which the kites must share with numerous ravens, and their replacement by plantations of the fashionable conifers could prove disastrous to the kites. In the damp meadows and wooded river valleys they hunt for young rabbits and moles, young corvids (much favoured), pigeons and black-headed gulls, in addition to lizards, frogs, snails, worms and insects; but the vole-ridden hilly parklands and upland sheep-walks are also vitally important, for almost half their round-the-year intake of food consists of sheep carrion, for which they must compete, again, with ravens and also buzzards. This abundant supply of carrion may indeed have been as crucial as protection in enabling the kites to survive in this Welsh valley. At one time losses due to feeding on the strychnine-poisoned carcases of foxes, crows and other carrion-eaters had reduced the colony to only three pairs, but in 1975 28 pairs reared 24 fledgelings – the highest number this century.

18 Man-Made Habitats

Sparrows

Man the cultivator with his cereal crops must have attracted house sparrows as commensals at an early date and they were probably well established in Britain by the time of the Roman occupation. The following passage from Bede's most famous tale concerning a heathen priest takes us back to Northumbria early in the seventh century:

> You are feasting with your ealdorman and thegns in winter-time; the fire is burning on the hearth in the middle of the hall and all inside is warm, while outside the wintry storms of rain and snow are raging; and a sparrow flies swiftly through the hall. It enters in at one door and quickly flies out through the other. For a few moments it is inside, the storm and wintry tempest cannot touch it, but after the briefest moment of calm, it flits from your sight, out of the wintry storm and into it again. So this life of man appears but for a moment, what follows or indeed what went before, we know not at all.

With easy pickings to be had in towns, particularly when oxen and horses provided the only means of transport, and with eaves and wall creepers furnishing ideal nesting sites, the sparrows took up permanent residence with urban man, though the juvenile population of sparrows in the smaller towns would emigrate temporarily in the late summer and autumn to the surrounding harvest fields. These, however, were visited mainly by the rural village sparrows:

> Whilst thousands in a flock for ever gay
> Loud chirping sparrows welcome on the day,
> And from the mazes of the leafy thorn
> Drop one by one upon the bending corn –

wrote Robert Bloomfield, a farm labourer's son, in *The Farmer's Boy* in 1799.

Being 'excellent food and a great restorer of decayed Nature', sparrows were indeed often encouraged in towns. According to Thomas Randolf in 1640:

> Another story makes waste chinne
> With breasts like Pots to nest young sparrows in.

He was referring no doubt to the unglazed Delftware pots that the Hollanders were using as sparrow traps as early as 1600, and which were probably introduced to Britain in the 1630s by Dutch engineers employed in draining the Fens. In Delft, which was a brewing centre, sparrows were a pest, and these pots, fashioned with a narrow entrance hole, were affixed to the walls of houses to function as nest-boxes from which the sparrows could easily be extracted. In Italy both sparrows and starlings were taken in this manner, as described in an early-seventeenth-century account:

> To catch those Starlings, which are accustomed to nest in roofs and buildings, it is usual to place against the wall of the place where they breed a vessel of unvarnished terra-cotta, made to resemble the wine bottles which the country folk use, having one side flat and the other spherical. A space is left open in the flat side of the vessel, sufficiently large to admit the insertion of a hand. When the 'Fiamingli' is placed in position, the spherical side faces, of course, outermost. When the Starlings or Sparrows which occupied the vessel have reared their progeny to a good size, the fowler takes down the vessel and extracts the young birds.

In England the nestling sparrows were removed when they were big enough to eat, and these trap-boxes were still in common use in Kent and Sussex – where they may have served the additional purpose of protecting thatched roofs – until late in the nineteenth century. Although the seventeenth-century ornithologist Francis Willughby declared that – '*Stares* are not eaten in *England* by reason of the bitterness of their flesh: the *Italians* and outlandish people are not so squeamish, but they can away with them, and make a dish of them for all that' – young starlings were in fact reared in similar pots and eaten by the nobility in England. Even the robin was 'esteemed a light and good meal'!

By the seventeenth century sparrows had spread throughout Britain, though they increased their area of occupation, particularly in Scotland, after 1800, and today the British population may number between seven and fourteen million. Rarely nesting more than a mile from human habitation, when they may do so in the branches of trees or in the sides of rooks' or magpies' nests, sparrows have followed man the food provider wherever he has gone – up the Highland railways to such bleak moorland halts as Dalnaspidal and Corrour, both more than

1,300 feet above sea-level, or reputedly down a coal-mine in Northumberland to nest several hundred feet underground and subsist on scraps from the miners; but though nesting in caves and on cliffs on some islands they have never or rarely colonised uninhabited islands. When, for example, the small Shetland island of Noss ceased to be permanently inhabited in 1939, and to be occupied during the summer months only by a single shepherd who did not keep poultry, the breeding sparrow population was reduced from scores or a few pairs to one pair. Nor did they colonise North Rona or St Kilda, where on Hirta they were replaced in the village by tree sparrows. In Britain the latter are predominantly rural birds, though locally common in the suburbs of some large towns; but on the Continent they live in most Scandinavian towns and associate with the house sparrows, while in southern Germany and the Swiss Alps, where there are no house sparrows, it is the tree sparrows that nest in the roofs of houses.

Martins

The widespread dispersal of the house sparrows may have been partly responsible for the marked decline in the house martin population in Britain during the past hundred years or more, because of the sparrows' habit of appropriating the martins' old nests before the latter return from their winter quarters in South Africa. Martins were still nesting in the Strand and the Fleet (already polluted with soot) in Gilbert White's day. Sand martins also 'swarmed' about the banks of the Thames below London Bridge at that time, though today a large proportion of the sand martins in Britain nest in such man-made habitats as sand-, gravel- or chalk-pits, while for the past fifty years drainage pipes have housed a permanent colony in the London area. However, as long ago as 1866 Stevenson was attributing the decrease of house martins, and to a lesser extent of swallows, in East Anglia to the diminishing supply of insects due to the drainage of water-meadows and fens. More recently a phenomenal fall in the numbers of martins nesting in Scottish towns and villages has coincided with the proliferation of tarmac roads, and therefore perhaps with a scarcity of muddy pools from which to obtain building material. But when one learns that a single pair of swifts, for example, may bring as many as twenty thousand small insects and spiders to their nestlings in one day, it appears probable that a major cause of the martins' decline in large towns must have been the reduction of winged insect food due to industrial pollution, and martins are indeed much more numerous in less polluted Ireland than in England, where they are now largely restricted to the smaller towns and villages. Clean-air measures and the creation of smokeless zones have resulted in both martins and swifts, and also warblers and tits, gradually spreading inwards from areas adjoining central London, and in martins nesting in inner London again after an absence of almost eighty years.

Insects

However, the most fascinating aspect of industrial pollution relates, not to birds but to insects, and has enabled us to witness the rare phenomenon of evolution actually in process. Since the 1860s as much as fifty tons of 'soot' has been deposited monthly on every square mile around some industrial zones, and much greater quantities of smaller particles have been airborne over hundreds of miles. As a result of this chemical pollution the lichens that covered most tree-trunks before the Industrial Revolution have been killed off or prevented from growing over large areas. But for thousands of years previously many insects had been evolving wing patterns that rendered them invisible to avian predators on the lichenous trunks and boughs on which they rested during the daytime. With the obliteration of the lichens the cryptic camouflage of these insects became instead highly conspicuous against the soot-blackened bark, exposing them to the danger of ultimately being exterminated by birds. Yet within little more than a hundred years almost the whole population of more than one hundred species of moths, and also some spiders and beetles, in manufacturing districts have been able to adopt an equally cryptic black coloration; while their caterpillars have become adapted to feeding on leaves polluted by toxic chemicals. This transformation has also taken place in industrial areas of France, Germany and south-east Europe, and is widespread in North America. The best-known example of this phenomenon is the peppered moth, whose usual colouring was formerly white, finely speckled with black, so that when resting on a trunk it resembled a patch of lichen. It was not until 1850 that a black specimen of this moth was caught – near Manchester, where previously only the peppered variety had been known; but by 1900 99 per cent of the Manchester peppered moths were of the black variety, and today the peppered variety is a rarity in that area.

There are two possible explanations of this phenomenon. On the one hand it could be argued that both peppered and black varieties have always existed, but that, when lichenous trees predominated, the black variety was prevented from becoming established in rural areas and reproducing in large numbers because it was more easily detected than the peppered by such birds as spotted flycatchers, nuthatches, song thrushes, robins or redstarts; but gained a survival advantage over the peppered variety in urban areas when these became polluted and the trees blackened. On the other hand, it could also be argued that the black variety is a mutant, of which under normal conditions the incidence is only one in about half a million; but since these black mutants invariably produce black progeny, the survival advantages of the latter in a polluted environment have enabled them to become the dominant variety. As H.B.D. Kettlewell has pointed out in *Animals*, melanism is common in regions where the hours of darkness are short during the summer, with the result that nocturnal insects are obliged to be on the wing during the periods of daylight. In Shetland

3. Light and Dark Varieties of Peppered Moths

a third of all the species of moths have black forms, while some of these in the relict Caledon Forest appear to be similar to those in present-day industrial Britain. The black form of the marbled beauty moth, for example, forms between 5 and 10 per cent of the population in the wholly unpolluted Black Wood of Rannoch, but a similar form comprises over 90 per cent of the population in much of industrial England.

Returning to the martins, before man-made sites became available they must have nested on inland crags and on sea cliffs and in sea caves, as some still do in Cornwall, but were quick to take advantage of man's buildings, for wherever there is a shooting lodge in the Highlands there you may be almost certain of finding a few pairs of martins, though the next colony may be many miles distant. The remotest lodge or, for that matter, farm steading, shepherd's cottage, sheep fank, bridge, dam, boathouse, old sawmill, abandoned township, forestry camp or quarry 1,500 feet up in the hills is also invariably tenanted in summer by its single pair of pied wagtails; and in 1961, after the Glen More ski-road had been opened, a cock wagtail arrived at the car park some 2,000 feet up on Cairn Gorm. At one time cliff-nesting martins were to be found all round Scottish coasts, but there has been a continuous decrease in both cliff- and cave-nesting since the latter half of the nineteenth century. Bolam has described these coastal colonies in *The Birds of Northumberland and the Eastern Borders:*

> In some of these stations a cove, or overhanging shelf of rock, affords corners to which typical nests can be affixed, and there they often appear crowded together, several sometimes touching one another; but narrow crevices between rocks, or weather-worn holes in the face of the stone, are often also occupied, and in these no more mud is used than is necessary to reduce the size of the entrance to the hole, or to partition off a section of the crevice-ledge. Sometimes a trifling breastwork of clay is all that represents the accustomed 'masonry', and one is left to ponder whether the Nuthatch-like practice of merely building-up the too large opening of a hole may not be the original nesting habit of the Martin, from which the semi-spherical nests represent the latest development. In olden days, when birds of prey were more numerous, their depredations would require more guarding against . . . A female Kestrel nearly drove the Martins away, from the persistent manner in which she raided their nests. . . While she was seen to obtain a foothold on a ledge, and extract a young martin from a nest built thereon, those nests beneath overhanging rocks were probably beyond her reach.

Swallows

Swallows also nested on sea-cliffs in various parts of Scotland and not uncommonly, according to Charles St John, in sea-caves in Morayshire (as swifts did in the Cromarty Rocks): 'In the latter situations the nest is formed perfectly similar to that of the martin, and fitted into a hollow or crevice of the rocks.' But Bolam knew of only one locality – near Berwick-upon-Tweed – where swallows nested on cliff ledges, hard by martins. One assumes that swallows were never very numerous in Britain until man introduced thatched huts and subsequently more substantial houses, farmsteads and collieries, preferably with chimneys, though such isolated buildings as the chapel and lighthouse tower on the Inner Farne island were also acceptable. In Gilbert White's time – and even today in some districts – swallows habitually nested five or six feet down the shafts of chimneys. This must have been a comparatively modern practice, for as late as 1577 William Harrison had noted 'the multitude of chimneys lately erected'. According to White, those chimneys in which a fire was constantly burning in the adjoining shaft were particularly favoured by the swallows, which were as indifferent to the smoke as those house martins and swifts that will fly through a smoke-cloud, apparently 'bathing' in it.

'Wonderful is the address which this adroit bird shows all day long in ascending and descending with security through so narrow a pass', wrote White of the chimney swallow:

When hovering over the mouth of the funnel, the vibration of her wings acting on the confined air occasion a rumbling like thunder . . . The progressive method by which the young are introduced into life is very amusing: first, they emerge from the shaft with difficulty enough, and often fall down into the room below: for a day or so they are fed on the chimney-top, and then are conducted to the dead leafless bough of some tree, where, sitting in a row, they are attended with great assiduity.

Swifts

Most swifts nest in buildings, particularly those where holes in the stonework of high walls and towers afford access to rafters; but sparrow holes in thatched roofs and the mud-cups of martins are occasionally used. Some, however, nest in quarries, and White – whose account of the swift's habits was the fullest until David Lack published his *Swifts in a Tower* in 1956 – mentioned that they did so in a chalk-pit at Odiham, in which they were still nesting early this century. But the swift's European relatives still nest mainly on crags and cliffs, with buildings of only secondary importance, and in Britain they formerly did so on inland crags in such localities as Dovedale and the Pennines, and in sea cliffs, particularly in the west and north, though Stevenson refers to them nesting in deep fissures in the chalk cliffs at Hunstanton, together with starlings and jackdaws. They are also reported to have bred in large numbers in the mountains of North Wales, and they have nested more than once in the 3,786-feet summit crags of Lochnagar in the Eastern Highlands. In the Rothiemurchus pine forest they occupied the old nest-holes of pied woodpeckers, and Bolam referred to one pair which, in the late nineteenth century, nested below an osprey's eyrie; but since there are no recent records of swifts nesting in trees, this habit peresumably lapsed with the virtual extinction of woodpeckers in the Highlands, though old woodpecker holes in pine trees remain the normal nesting site of swifts in Lapland.

Black Redstarts

The most recent colonisers on a small scale of English towns have been the black redstarts. Although they had not been recognised in Britain prior to 1819, they had become frequent birds of passage on south and east coasts by the middle of that century, and this passage was associated with sporadic attempts to breed in Durham in 1845 and in Sussex in 1909. Finally in 1923 they began to nest regularly in Sussex coastal towns and annually in London three years later; but it was, ironically, the Luftwaffe that was responsible for boosting the size of the London colony of these redstarts – though there were probably never more than thirty or forty pairs in any one year – for an environment of bombed buildings and bulldozed clearings apparently represented an ideal habitat, in which they could nest on ledges in gutted buildings and feed on ants, flies and other insects among the acres of rubble.

When tidying up the chaos and rebuilding got under way after the war the number of redstarts nesting in central London appeared to decrease, but it was subsequently discovered that they had in fact moved quarters and were concentrated in heavy-industry areas, particularly in power-stations and gasworks.

39. A Cock Black Redstart by its Nest in a Bombed London Building

At first sight black redstarts appear most unlikely birds to have colonised English towns and ultimately a metropolis such as London – just as a member of the montane accentors was an unlikely colonist of heavily forested Britain – for, like rock thrushes and crag martins, these redstarts were, according to Murton, originally inhabitants of the warm mountainous regions of the southern Palearctic but spread northwards after the final glaciation to the mountains of central Europe, to which they were confined as a breeding species. However, although the high alp pastures, with their screes, rocks, lichens and dwarf juniper, were their summer home, they wintered in villages and farms on the plains; and when in the middle of the nineteenth century they began to disperse north over Germany, reaching Jutland later that century and Scandinavia in the 1940s, they adapted to breeding in a lowland habitat by utilising man-made buildings as nesting sites in lieu of alpine crags and outcrops.

Asiatic Collared Doves

During the past twenty years it has also been fascinating to watch the colonisation of Britain by a bird that may prove to be as successful a

0. Collared Doves

commensal as the house sparrow and as numerous as the fulmar petrel. The Asiatic collared doves may have originated in northern India and the Himalayas, though we first hear of them in Istanbul in the middle of the sixteenth century; and that was the limit of their westerly dispersal for some three hundred years until they appeared in Bulgaria in 1834. By the beginning of this century they had reached Yugoslavia and Albania, but it was not until about 1930 that a population explosion occurred and another westerly dispersal began. The vanguard of this reached France in 1950, Belgium in 1952, Norway in 1954 and finally Britain in 1955, when collared doves were first reported from Cromer, and two years later from Moray. By the 1960s they had reached the Outer Isles, Ireland, Shetland and the Scillies, and the British population may now total thirty or forty thousand pairs.

Their twentieth-century advance across southern Europe may have been accelerated by the network of pylons and power-cables, which served as perching sites for feeding and courting birds – as they did for various shrikes. Throughout their dispersal they have taken advantage of ecological niches provided by man, in the form of parks, gardens, cemeteries and farm steadings in or near towns and villages, and have concentrated in large feeding communities where grain and other seed spillage associated with poultry or malting or in docks is plentiful throughout the year, providing that trees or hedgerows are available for nesting. In these niches the collared doves do not compete with turtle doves, which are predominantly birds of open arable land with a scattering of hedgerows and copses, and to a lesser degree of gorse-covered heaths and woodland edge, and which feed largely on the seeds of fine grasses and especially on the seed capsules of fumitory. They do not compete with stockdoves, which are primarily birds of open parklands and warrens, and to a small extent coastal cliffs, and which do not build nests in trees but lay their eggs in holes in hollow trees or cliffs or in rabbit burrows. Nor do they compete with wood pigeons, which are essentially woodland birds, feeding on the buds, seeds and flowers of trees and, in winter, on the leaves of such farm crops as turnips and clover.

Pigeons

Some of the niches that the collared doves have occupied would have been pre-empted by feral pigeons had nesting sites on buildings been accessible, but there are very few records of these pigeons nesting in trees. Murton has suggested that the decline of the dovecot culture throughout Europe, and the consequent removal of artificial nesting sites for feral pigeons, may have been one of the factors that facilitated the westward colonisation by collared doves. Feral pigeons, including the motley town pigeons and the various breeds of homers, are all descended from wild rock doves, which nested in sea caves and collected seeds, seaweed and molluscs from the cliff top, tide-line and beach, and also flew inland to feed on cultivated fields. The rock doves were farmed from an early date, ledges being erected in the doo-caves to permit the collection of the young doves, which were then either eaten or reared for breeding stock. Later, the Norman lords supplemented their rabbit warrens with large dovecots, and these became a feature in rural communities. So important indeed were the cots as a reservoir of fresh meat that by 1617 there were no fewer than 36,000 pairs of dovecot pigeons in Fife alone, and in the previous century a third offence of destroying a dovecot had been penalised in Scotland by 'hanging to death'. Subsequently, every squire maintained a loft at the expense of the peasants' crops, but the number of lofts declined in the late eighteenth century when farmers reckoned wheat more valuable than pigeon meat. The feral population in the towns, however, continued to increase and, according to Murton, enormous numbers on the waterfronts of such towns as Liverpool and Birkenhead, and in the Manchester docks, are now entirely dependent on man's provisions, feeding throughout the year on the grain and other spillages associated with the handling and storage of food cargoes. But other stocks of feral pigeons have rejoined the wild rock doves, with the result that while a hundred years ago there were pure-bred flocks of rock doves in south-west, west and northern England, today, if any such flocks remain, they exist only in north and west Scotland and in Ireland.

19 The Farmer's Birds

As a result of the Enclosures there was an immense increase in the acreage of permanent grass and of cultivated land. This, like the new plantations and gardens, further encouraged the dispersal of birds from their former woodland habitat. Although the Enclosures may have benefited foxes, rabbits and rodents, there was another aspect of them, the immediate impact of which on a hypersensitive countryman is revealed in *Helpstone Green*, which the Northamptonshire poet John Clare wrote between 1808 and 1819:

> Ye injur'd fields, ye once were gay,
> When nature's hand display'd
> Long waving rows of willows grey,
> And clumps of hawthorn shade;
> But now, alas! your hawthorn bowers
> All desolate we see,
> The spoilers' axe their shade devours,
> And cuts down every tree.

Later he returned to this theme:

> There once were days, the woodman knows it well,
> When shades e'en echoed with the ringing thrush;
> There once were hours, the ploughman's tale can tell,
> When morning's beauty wore its earliest blush,
> How woodlarks caroll'd from each stumpy bush;
> Lubin himself has mark'd them soar and sing:
> The thorns are gone, the woodlark's song is hush,
> Spring more resembles winter now than spring,
> The shades are banish'd all – the birds have took to wing.

Nevertheless, the new farmlands provided feeding grounds for a diversity of birds – finches, pipits, larks, buntings, starlings, rooks, lapwings – and, when the hedges and hedgerow trees matured, nesting cover, roosting places and song perches. The result was that by the late eighteenth century England, and especially the Midlands, relieved of the heavy forest canopy, had become a land of singing birds, in contrast to the hedgeless plains of France with their silent springs. Today, more than half of Britain's land surface consists of arable land or permanent pasture, about one-third of common, moorland and heath, and less than one-tenth of woods and forests; but most woodland species have adapted to life in the new habitats of farmland, hedgerow, park, orchard and garden, and their overall numbers must greatly have increased.

Partridges

However, the post-war years have been associated with yet further radical changes in the rural landscape. In this era of feverish technological experiment hardly a day has passed without the introduction of some agricultural innovation. Some of the innovations have proved harmless to wildlife: others harmful. Prairie farming in eastern Britain, entailing the grubbing up of endless miles of hedgerow trees, has resulted in a considerable reduction in the numbers of such typical hedgerow species as whitethroats, yellowhammers and chaffinches wherever arable farmland predominates, while the levelling of hedgebanks and destruction of thick-bottomed hedgerows have made it very difficult for our native partridges to find suitable nesting sites, with the result that they are forced to nest in hayfields or silage crops, where their eggs and often the sitting bird too are destroyed by the blades of

41. A Red-legged Partridge

the tractor-hauled mower in May or June. Heaven knows what the new rotary cutter must do, whirring at 2,000 revolutions a minute! Whereas, with horse mowers and enough gamekeepers to mark nests, these could be avoided by the pre-war farmhand, who was more patient than his modern labourer-cum-mechanic counterpart. But more detrimental to partridge survival has been the introduction of insecticides and herbicides, for while during the first week of its life 99 per cent of a young partridge's feed consists of insects, and only 5 per cent of vegetable matter, by the fourth week this ratio has been reversed. Thus, during the first week its insect food is polluted or destroyed by insecticides, and by the fourth week its vegetable food is being killed by herbicides; while those chicks that survive late cold springs may have to contend with stubble-burning, followed almost immediately by ploughing. Moreover, on some farms shooting may be prolonged into January when the adults may already be pairing and reluctant to move out of their territories to escape the guns.

It is therefore not surprising that partridges are now rare birds over considerable areas of Britain and fewer in numbers than ever before in their history. Since the end of the eighteenth century the East Anglian stock of partridges in particular has also had to complete with the red-legged 'Frenchmen', whose food is very similar, though there is no actual evidence that our native partridges have been evicted from any of their haunts by the red-legs. Attempts were made to introduce the latter to Britain as early as 1673, but they were not established successfully until about 1770, when thousands of eggs were set under bantams in Suffolk. On the light dry sandy soil of that county the red-legs thrived and, with frequent subsequent introductions, have now become permanent wild residents as far west as Wales and north to Yorkshire, though in Europe their range does not extend north of Brittany and north-west Italy.

Pheasants

Only a brief reference is required to pheasants, since the vast majority are still raised under artificial conditions. Although there is no mention of them in Britain earlier than 1059, the purple-necked variety from the western Caucasus was almost certainly reared in Roman Britain, and bones excavated at Corbridge are reported to be definitely those of pheasants; but none of the Roman birds appear to have gone wild, and the sixteenth-century ballad, *The Battle of Otterburn*, includes perhaps the first reference to wild pheasants:

The Fawcon and the Fesaunt both
Amongst the holtes on hee –

while towards the end of the next century Nicholas Cox described, in *The Gentleman's Recreation*, netting pheasants in thick young copses not visited by men or cattle, adding that they were never to be found in open fields.

It was the end of the eighteenth century before the ring-necked pheasant – a native of the reed-beds, paddy fields and scrub-covered hills of eastern China – was introduced. It is rather surprising that this hardy family has not thrived more vigorously in Britain, though it is true that in the Grampians the odd hen pheasant may be found sitting on eggs in a rushy place among the heather more than 1,400 feet above sea-level.

Corncrakes

More noticeable to country folk than the decline of the partridge has been the widespread loss of the vociferous corncrake. It has been suggested that nesting corncrakes were in fact always sparsely distributed over southern England, for William Turner said that he had seen them only in Northumberland, while Gilbert White accounted them rare in the Selborne district; but the latter added that they had formerly abounded in the bean fields in north Wiltshire and in the Oxford meadows, and Richard Jefferies described them as numerous in the vicinity of the South Downs. However, they had ceased to breed in East Anglia before 1900, in southern England and the east Midlands by the time of the First World War, and during the next 25 years deserted Wales, western England, and eastern Scotland where they had been very common in St John's day. Since they have decreased over an area stretching from the Faeroes to the Channel Islands some climatic factor may be involved, but it is difficult to believe that mowing hay with machines instead of scythes, and cutting grass earlier for silage, have not contributed to their decrease – as may perhaps the use of artificial fertilisers instead of dung, resulting in a diminution of insect food; and it is significant that by the advent of the Second World War some 85 per cent of corncrake haunts in Britain were being cut regularly by machines.

Some observations by L. S. V. and U. M. Venables in the Shetlands after the war seem highly relevant. Their impression was that in those islands corncrakes were most densely concentrated in those areas where the cultivation was intensive, where the rotation of grasses (usually rye) was a regular feature of the cropping cycle, and where stock was not allowed to graze over the arable land during the winter. They noted that it was the first and second weeks of May before craking birds settled in. At that date meadow grass was scarce – grazed low by sheep and held back by salt-laden winter gales – while the rigs intended for bere, oats, potatoes, cabbages and roots were utterly bare. Patches of rotation grass provided ley for the best cover available and acted as magnets to the incoming birds, which needed both immediate shelter for themselves and a luxurious growth in which to establish their nests. At that date the only alternative to rotation grasses was provided by occasional areas of coarse meadow grass which for some reason had been ungrazed, but which in a wet season did not dry out sufficiently for early occupation by corncrakes. However, ley grass was an unfortunate choice of habitat, for it was the earliest crop to be cut and was mown during July, exposing eggs and many broods only a few days old. When the grass was cut by hand the mowers kept a sharp watch for eggs or chicks, and if the eggs were seen in time the usual practice was to leave an uncut patch round the nest. In some instances the incubating bird would return and succeed in hatching the eggs. If chicks were found they were caught and carried to some adjacent cover where (in most cases at least) the adults found them, while adults and large young were merely driven out of the crop and not driven to and butchered in the isolated central patch as happened with the decreasing-circle method of mechanical mowing. Where grass was cut by tractor the men still kept a bright look-out in the old tradition, but frequently some of the chicks were killed before the brood was noticed. An attempt might be made to leave a patch of uncut grass round a nest of eggs, but such nests were rarely seen before it was too late to save them.

Lapwings

Lapwings, which have been associated with the farming landscape since Saxon times, have benefited from the extension of agriculture and, with milder climatic conditions, have colonised northwards over Europe to the Faeroes and Iceland and recently to Finland and Norway. However, they too have decreased in Britain since the 1840s; but there is no evidence that this decline has in their case been due either to mechanisation or to the use of chemicals, and the slump in their numbers during the nineteenth century was certainly partly the result of excessive egg-taking, which was heavy throughout Britain. In 1821, for example, 160 dozen eggs were taken from a Norfolk marsh by one man, while in 1834 a Great Yarmouth game dealer was despatching six or seven hundred eggs a week to the London market throughout the season. But the main cause of their decline was the reduction in acreage by enclosures, drainage and cultivation, of vast tracts of heath and marshland, and a corresponding increase in ploughland. Lapwings prefer to make their nest-scrapes on ground with a modicum of cover. Therefore in theory ploughland should provide them with the ideal nesting habitat, but in practice its use results in a regular annual loss of thousands of eggs and chicks when the land is being drilled, harrowed and rolled.

Goldfinches

It could be argued that the decrease of the goldfinch in Britain coincided with the improvement in agricultural skills from 1870 to 1920 and the complementary thinning out of thistles and other weeds. William Cobbett was aware that thistle seeds were the favourite food of the goldfinch, and when near Malmsbury in Wiltshire on 11 September 1826, he noted that:

> This seed is just now dead ripe. The thistles are all cut and carried away from the fields by the harvest, but they grow alongside the roads; and, in this place, great quantities. So that the goldfinches were got here in flocks, and, as they continued to fly along before me, for nearly half a mile . . . I do believe I had, at last, a flock of ten thousand flying before me.

A thousand perhaps in the ordinary man's language!

E. M. Nicholson observed that in Ireland goldfinches were scarce on the peat and acid rock where thistles were also scarce, but extremely common on the limestone and other soils favourable to thistles. He deduced, therefore, that better farming rather than the activities of bird-catchers were responsible for the goldfinch's decline, since linnets, which were equally persecuted, but which did not rely on thistles for food, did not increase appreciably during the agricultural depression after the 1920s. This was a logical deduction, but did not take into account the fact that while goldfinches are now relatively common in most parts of Britain, despite the general improvement in farming standards and the widespread use of herbicides, they are still thin on the ground in most parts of Ireland, though they have increased since the Wild Birds Protection Acts of 1930 and 1931 declared bird-catching illegal. When one considers that a single bird-catcher is reported to have taken 3,000 goldfinches in one season in North Wales, and that 132,000 were said to be caught annually in the 1860s near Worthing, the traffic would appear to have been sufficient to depress the British goldfinch population, for there is no evidence that any large numbers of Continental goldfinches migrate through either Wales or Sussex.

Bird-Catching for Food

We have seen that there was a deep appreciation of Nature among some early clerics and poets and even hunters, and, as Nicholson has said, the birds so freely mentioned in the ballads must have been universally known: 'They appear quite naturally and spontaneously, as if everyone understood allusions to birds which were for a long time afterwards to be no more than empty names.' Nevertheless, birds to most men in Merrie England were primarily a source of food – necessarily so in the case of the common man, fashionably so for the rich; for as Polydore Vergil, who lived in England for several years after 1501, wrote:

> The cheefe foode of the Englishman consisteth in fleshe . . . Of wilde burdes these are most delicate, partriches, pheasaunts, quayles, owsels, thrushes and larkes. This last burde, in winter season, the wether being not too owtragios, dothe waxe wonderus fatte, at which time a wonderful nombrs of them is caughte, so that of all others they cheefle garnishe menns tables.

They did indeed: twelve thousand being taken before noon one day on the Sussex downs and despatched to London and Paris markets, though Dunstable Downs was the Mecca of the lark-catchers. The toll taken of small birds for food, and to a lesser extent for caging, right up until the earlier decades of this century, must have depressed their numbers significantly, even if, as in the case of some species such as larks, a considerable proportion of those caught were no doubt birds of passage or winter visitors from northern Europe. The right to catch larks by *low-belling* was so highly valued as to be restricted in practice to the owners of land. Elaborate instructions were available to the would-be 'low-beller'. In *A Jewell for Gentrie*, dated 1614, we learn that the fowler should:

> Goe with a great light of Cressets or ragges of linen dipt in Tallow that will make a goode light, and you must have a panne or plate, made like a Lanterne, to carrye your light in, which must have a great socket to hold a great light, and carrie it before you on your brest, with a Bell in your other hand of a great Bignesse, made in manner like a Cowbell, but of greater bignes, and you must ring it allwayes after one order, with two to goe with Nets one on each side of him that carries the Bell, and what with the Light that so doth amaze them, and the Bell that so doth astonish them, they will, when you come neere them, turn up their white bellies, which you shall quickly perceive, then lay your nets on them and take them; but the Bell must not stint going: for if it cease, then the birds will flye up if there be any more nigh. This is a good way to catch Larkes, Woodcockes, and Partriches, and all other land-Birdes.

In *Hunger's Prevention: or the Whole Art of Fowling by Water and Land*, published in 1655, Gervase Markham enlarged on this art of low-belling:

> After the night hath covered the face of the earth (which commonly 'tis about eight of the clock at night), the Ayre being mild, and the Moon not shining, you shall take your Low-Bell, which is a Bell of such a reasonable size as a man may well carry it in one hand, and having a deep, hollow and sad sound, for the more quick and shrill it is the worse it is, and the more sad and solemne, the better: and with this Bell you shall also have a net (of a small mesh) at least twenty yards deep, and so broad that it may cover five or six ordinary hands or more, according as you have company to carry it (for the more ground it covers, the more is your sport, and the richer the prey that is taken); with these instruments you shall go into some stubble field, either Wheat, Rye, or Barley, but the Wheat is the best, and he which carrieth the Bell shall goe the formost, and toll the Bell as Hee goeth along, so solemny as may be, letting it but now and then knock on both sides; then shall follow the net, being

borne up at each corner and on each side by sundry persons; then another man shall carry an old yron Cresset, or some other vessel of stone or yron in which you shall have good store of sinders or burning coales (but not blazing), and at these you shall light bundles of dry Straw, Hay, Stubble, Linkes, Torches, or any other substance that will blaze, and then having spread and pitcht your Nette where you think any Game is (having all your lights blazing), with noyses and poles beat up all that are under the Net, so as you may take them at your pleasure: as Partridges, Rayles, Larkes, Quailes . . . which done, you shall suddenly extinguish your lights, and then proceed forward and lay your Net in another place.

Larks could also be taken with clap-nets from mid-September to mid-November, by which gloomy season the birds would no longer 'dare' or strike at the revolving mirrors, which were placed in the centre of the nets and controlled by a cord. According to Markham, a triangular body-piece of mirror was studded with 'about twenty small pieces of looking-glasses, and paynt all the spare wood between them of a very bright red colour, which in the continual motion and turning about, will give such a glorious reflection, that the wanton birds cannot forbear but will play about it with admiration till they be taken.'

Nearer to our own times fashion decreed that wheatears should be in every dish, and William Yarrell, writing in 1843 and quoting Pennant, states that about 22,000 wheatears were taken annually on the downs between Eastbourne and Beachy Head during their autumn passage from the third week in July to the third week in September, despite the fact that this was a migration of individual birds and twos and threes, not of flocks: 'As they are then fat and of good colour, it is customary to dress them by dozens at the inns of the numerous watering-places on the Sussex coast.' The wheatears were trapped by the shepherds and herdsmen, and since a shepherd and his boy might look after between five and seven hundred traps, it was possible for them to catch as many as 84 dozen birds in a day. According to Yarrell:

The Wheatear trap is formed by cutting an oblong piece of turf from the surface, about eight inches by eleven, and six inches thick, which is to be taken up in a solid mass, and laid in the contrary way . . . over the hole, thus forming a hollow chamber beneath it. Besides this chamber, two other openings are also cut in the turf, about six inches wide and of greater length, which lead into the chamber at opposite ends that the bird may run in under the turf through either of them. A small straight stick, sharpened at both ends . . . is fixed in an upright position a little on one side of the middle of the square chamber; the stick supports two open running loops of twisted horse-hair placed vertically across the line of passage from either entrance to the opposite outlet, and the bird attempting to run through is almost certain to get his head into one of these loops and be caught by the neck: upon the least alarm, even the shadow of a passing cloud, the birds run beneath the clod and are taken.

Starlings

Starlings were also taken in clap-nets or by means of fastening a limed string to a live bird and then releasing it, when, on it flying up and joining a flock of its fellows, the string would adhere to some of these. So long as Britain was heavily forested, starlings cannot have been very widespread, for they are essentially grassland feeders, equipped to part the herbage with mandibles agape and snap up large numbers of leather-jackets and insects. They probably originated on the steppes of Asia, where they must presumably have nested under piles of stones as some do in Britain, and as the rose-winged starlings still do. Their invasion of towns must be comparatively recent, for though there were references to large flocks of starlings roosting in the reed-beds of the Fens late in the eighteenth century, it was the 1890s before they first began to commute from the London suburbs to roost in the trees of St James's Park, and some years after that before they moved to their still-existing roost, composed mainly of British-breeding residents, on buildings in the West End. There was in fact little urban roosting in England until

2. Starling Fledgelings in Their Nest

the early 1930s, though there were enormous roosts on thorn plantations within the precincts of such garden cities as Letchworth some thirty miles out of London.

There have, however, been resident populations of starlings in sparsely wooded Caithness and Sutherland as far back as records go. In 1630 there were reported to be great numbers of them in Sutherland, and in the summer of 1848 St John found that on the island of Handa the turf walls of the houses, abandoned by their emigrating inhabitants earlier that spring, were honeycombed with the holes of countless starlings. On the predominantly treeless islands of the Outer Hebrides, where the nineteenth-century naturalist William MacGillivray found a pair nesting among rock-doves below a sea eagle's eyrie on Ben Capval, and on North Rona and the Orkney Islands colonies of starlings have been established for so long that the juveniles have acquired plumage distinctions recognisable in the field. At one time the Orcadians encouraged them to nest in their houses by providing holes for them: just as today almost every house in the Faeroes still puts up nesting boxes for starlings – a legacy from the days when young starlings were considered a delicacy in this part of Europe too. In an island environment they may nest under boulders and in rabbit holes and the burrows of storm petrels, and a considerable proportion of Scotland's starlings still nest and roost in cliffs and sea caves, and forage with small wading birds in the storm-piled heaps of seaweed.

Initially, starlings did not benefit from the Enclosures, since the young hedgerows offered no suitable sites for hole-nesting birds. Moreover, the clearance of woodland, entailing the destruction of old timber, also deprived them of nesting holes – as it did the woodpeckers – though in Scotland some starlings built open nests in trees, especially yew, if holes were not available. It is only within the last hundred years or so that starlings have become common in many parts of west and north Britain, for it was around 1830 before there was any record of a starling nesting in Devon, 1855 before any did so in Cornwall and between 1833 and 1860 before they did so in Wales, where they are still uncommon breeding birds in parts of the west. Previously they had been winter visitors only to these regions. That was also the case in the West Riding of Yorkshire, where that unconventional but highly successful conservationist, Charles Waterton, writing in the first half of the nineteenth century, noted that for many years the bulk of the wintering starlings had left the district around Walton Hall in the spring because, as he believed, of the lack of nesting accommodation due to the widespread felling of old timber. However, half a dozen pairs habitually nested within his walled park, and this small colony he increased by excavating 24 holes in an old ruin, all of which were occupied by starlings the following winter.

In north Britain the history of the starlings is confused. In Bewick's time in the late eighteenth century they were very rare in Northumberland, but by the 1830s had become numerous. In southern Scotland by contrast they were common at the end of the eighteenth century, but had almost disappeared by the 1840s, when their status was mainly that of a rare passage migrant, and a live pair sold for the considerable sum of 1*s*. Sir Walter Scott, whose life spanned the years 1771 to 1832, recalled that when he was four or five years old and staying in Roxburghshire, a large pigeon house was almost destroyed by starlings, which were then common, but that later in his life they were seldom seen; for by then any woodlands left by the early farmers and the Cistercians had been cleared to make way for arable farms and to accommodate the immense flocks of sheep. But by the middle of the nineteenth century the trees planted by the Improvers were approaching maturity and offering nesting holes, while at the same time large numbers of barns and farm buildings were being erected, and reports of starlings recolonising Scotland as a breeding species began to come in. A general colonisation of the Highlands had begun in the 1840s, when St John stated that they nested commonly in trees and buildings in Moray, and during the second half of that century there was a rapid and widespread dispersal throughout Scotland. It has been suggested that this extension of the starlings' range may have been facilitated by the widespread replacement of arable land by permanent pasture during the agricultural depressions, and it is true that their increase in the Lake District coincided with the conversion of mosses and heather into pasture and arable; but in fact there has been an overall loss of more than four million acres of permanent grassland in Britain during the past hundred years, while the extensive conversion of pasture into arable during the last war has not resulted in any apparent decrease in their numbers in any part of Britain. Moreover, starlings have now spread all over Europe to wherever man has settled, as far north as Iceland and sub-arctic latitudes. Thus, while changes in land use may have influenced starling populations regionally, their far-reaching colonisation of western Europe would appear to have been actuated, as in the case of the blackbird and some other species, primarily by climatic factors.

Rooks

Rooks, like starlings, are typical steppe birds, avoiding mountainous regions, though regularly visiting such uplands as Dartmoor and the Cheviots to forage during the summer months after the young birds have fledged. Their presence in densely forested Britain must therefore have originally been restricted to such areas as the chalk downs of southern England cleared by the early Neolithic husbandmen. However, as early as 1348 the monks of Durham were already taking measures to thin out the rooks on their arable land, and in 1424 an Act for the control of rooks was passed in Scotland:

> Item. Therefore as men consider that Rooks building in churchyards, orchards, or trees do great damage upon corn, it is ordained that they whom such trees pertain to, do let them build, and suffer

43. A Rookery in March

> on no wise that the young ones fly away, and when it is proved that they build and the young be flown, and the nests be found in the trees at May-day, the trees shall be forfeit to the King.

In 1533 Henry VIII brought in an Act under which day-nets or clap-nets were to be kept in every parish for the destruction of the excessive numbers of rooks, jackdaws and crows. Twenty years later Gesner noted that rooks were so numerous in Britain that they caused havoc in the corn-fields, and during Elizabeth's reign Henry's Act was revived to include not only corvines, for which churchwardens were authorised to pay head-money, but also bullfinches, woodpeckers (!) and king-fishers, buzzards, harriers, ospreys and (somewhat surprisingly) kites, together with cormorants and shags. According to that insufferable wiseacre Gervase Markham crow-nets were to be laid:

> Before or neere unto Barne doores where Corne is a thrashing, or in any such places where Corne hath been winnowed and the chaff remaining, with which you shall ever observe to cover and hide the Nets assoone as it is laid, so as it may not be seen, and then assoone as the flocks of birds come, and are scraping amongst the chaffe, you

> lying aloof off conceald, with the coard in your hand, shall sodenly draw it and overturne the net upon the birds, by which at one pull you may take . . . Crowes, pigeons, Kites, Buzzards, and such like ravenous birds.

Alternatively, the net could be set 'in any stubble field upon the Corn lands, provided the stubble cover the Net so as it is not perceived'.

But even in the sixteenth century there were those who had misgivings about exterminating rooks:

> From this our countrymen doubt whether they do not do more good to the land when they take worms and the pests of fruit and corn than they do harm to mankind when they devour grain and the food of men,

wrote John Caius, a colleague of William Turner; and that would be a fair summary of the modern attitude towards rooks, which are beneficial to grassland, ridding it of leather-jackets and wireworms, but may damage seed-corn and root crops by breaking down the drills. Now that the modern short-strawed varieties of corn are harvested early and do not stand in stooks, the rooks can only glean the grain lost in combining, and Robert Bloomfield's lines at the end of the eighteenth century no longer hold good:

> But still unsafe the big swoln grain below,
> A fav'rite morsel with the Rook and Crow.
> From field to field the flock increasing goes
> To level crops most formidable foes.
> Their danger well the wary plunderers know
> And place a watch on some conspicuous bough.

Although the staggering total of 76,655 rooks were reported to have been killed in the Earl of Haddington's woods in East Lothian between 1779 and 1793, their population in fact increased enormously in Britain (and also in Holland) during the first half of the present century, and by the end of the war there were about 3 million, including between 1¾ and 2 million in England, 200,000 in Wales and 750,000 in Scotland; but in recent years there has been a substantial decrease in their numbers in some parts of the country, halving their total population. The reasons for this have not been established, but toxic seed-dressings and the widespread incidence of Dutch elm disease must have contributed to this decline, while many juveniles must be killed by traffic now that rooks have become daily visitors to main roads at all seasons of the year, though what food they pick up on the tarmac remains a mystery to this observer.

Much the largest concentrations of rooks are in the favourable corn-growing, stock-rearing and adequately wooded terrain of eastern Scotland from Berwickshire to Aberdeenshire. There are no rookeries in

England comparable to the one at Hatton Castle in Aberdeenshire with its maximum of nearly seven thousand nests, and there are several more rookeries in that county containing more than a thousand nests. Given the requisite population of rooks in the surrounding countryside, the size of a rookery – which may contain no more than a dozen nests or even a single one – would seem to depend on the nature of the terrain and the type of tree available. Thus the majority of rookeries are sited below 400 feet, and in most regions deciduous trees are preferred to evergreens, despite the fact that in Cornwall, where the choice is about evenly divided, twice as many of the old nests survive the winter storms in evergreens than in deciduous trees. Groves of elms are the most popular, holding, for example, 90 per cent of the rookeries in Oxfordshire and almost 80 per cent in Gloucestershire, whereas less than 20 per cent are in oaks. This being the case, it will be interesting to observe the effect of the Dutch elm disease on the future siting of rookeries in such localities as Huntingdonshire, where there are few alternatives to elms. Kestrels, for whom elms provide almost the only available nesting trees in parts of southern England, will also be affected; as will herons, whose population is now at a peak after a series of open winters. At the largest British heronry of 180 nests in Kent the herons are gradually moving to nearby oaks as the elms die; but at a smaller heronry on Osea Island in the Blackwater estuary their nests are at present exposed among the dead branches of stricken elms. Such exposure could put the young herons at risk, for the fact that many heronries are built in Scots pines suggests that the shelter provided by a leafy canopy may be essential.

20 Nor Does the Fowler Desist from Beguiling Birds

Here lies the Decoyman who lived like an otter,
Dividing his time betwixt land and water;
His hide he oft soaked in the waters of Perry,
Whilst Aston old beer his spirits kept cherry.
Amphibious his life, Death was puzzled to say
How to dust to reduce such well-moistened clay;
So Death turned Decoyman and 'coyed him to land,
Where he fixed his abode till quite dried to the hand;
He then found him fitting for crumbling to dust,
And here he lies mouldering as you and I must.

Epitaph on Andrew Williams 1692-1776

Swans, cranes, pelicans and various species of ducks were, as we have seen, breeding in the marshes around the Glastonbury lake-village in the Vale of Avalon some two thousand years ago. There may also have been pelicans in the Fens, where fossils have been obtained from Cambridgeshire and Norfolk. The problem is – why did the pelicans, which were of the grey or Dalmatian species become extinct as British-breeding birds at some time between the Iron Age and the Dark Ages, while cranes survived in the Fens at least as late as 1590 and in Scotland until the eighteenth century? Were the Romans, with their drainage projects in the Fens, responsible for the disappearance of the pelicans from them, and possibly also from Glastonbury? Or was this brought about by the increasingly dry climate after the wet Atlantic period?

After the departure of the Romans the Fens reverted to their previous state, for according to the old Cambridge Natural History their drainage works took the form of a 'series of great sea-banks to keep out the tides, and in so doing interfered with the river outlets, which in course of time became choked with silt, and overflowing their banks rendered the area more of a morass than before.' In the twelfth century a monk, Thomas of Ely, writing in his chronicle *Liber Eliensis*, described the country around the Isle of Ely as:

> beset by great meres and fens as though by a strong wall: In our isle . . . the ploughman has not taken his hand from the plough, nor has the hunter cast aside his arrow, nor does the fowler desist from beguiling birds.

Thomas alludes in his chronicle to coots, grebes, cormorants, herons and 'numberless' geese and duck: 'At midwinter or when the birds moult their quills I have seen them caught by the hundred, or even by three hundreds more or less, sometimes they are taken in nets and snares as well as by bird-lime.' He also refers to a 'multitude' of red deer and roebuck, goats, hares, otters, polecats, weasels and stoats. He does not, however, mention cranes, though the Saxons were hawking 'croen' or 'cornoch' in Mercia as early as the middle of the ninth century, and we know that they were still breeding at Hickling in 1543, for William Turner stated that: 'Cranes, moreover, breed in England in marshy places. I myself have very often seen their pipers.' They were apparently still numerous in Norfolk during the next century, but probably mainly as winter visitors, for although Willughby referred to great flocks in the Fens, he did not know whether they still bred in England.

The multitudes of wildfowl and other game were probably already being significantly depleted by fowlers with nets, snares and crossbows in Thomas' day, for in the next century according to William Harrison:

> This enormity bred great troubles in King John's day, insomuch that, going in progress about the tenth of his reign, he found little or no game wherewith to . . . exercise his falcons. Wherefore . . . he restrained all manner of hawking or taking of fowl throughout England for a season whereby the land within few years was thoroughly replenished again.

As early as 1300 a Commission was set up to enquire into the harrying of spoonbills' 'eyries', and later that century it was made a criminal offence to carry the eggs of bitterns out of the Isle of Ely. Henry VIII complained strongly about the practice of capturing wildfowl when they were in the moult and unable to fly, and in 1534 passed an Act prohibiting the taking of the eggs of cranes, herons, spoonbills, bitterns and bustards from 31 May to 31 August. Seventeen years later the shooting of 'Wylde Fowlis' with firearms was prohibited in Scotland under pain of death, and in 1597 the use of 'girnis' was also banned.

Turner saw spoonbills nesting with herons in Norfolk, and we know that at that time there were also colonies of spoonbills in the Bishop of London's park at Fulham and in west Sussex. The following century

44 A Bittern

Sir Thomas Browne, after noting in his *Natural History of Norfolk* that the platea or shovelards, as he called them, built their nests in the tops of tall trees, added significantly that: 'They come in March and are shot by fowlers not for their meat butt the handsomeness of the same.' They probably bred for the last time in Britain in 1667 – on the Orwell in Suffolk – shortly after the Dutch engineers had completed their drainage works in the Fens.

The concern of royalty at the decline in the numbers of wildfowl was no doubt partly a gut reaction to the loss of choice dishes. The bittern, which the medieval poets and prosemen always referred to, under one or other of the 38 forms of its name, as the one bird most typical of the 'fenny' lands, was, for example, greatly esteemed as a table-bird. It continued to be so, despite the modicum of flesh on its bones, until the eighteenth century when the fenmen dined on roast 'bottley bump' every Sunday; but though bitterns were then common enough to sell for 1*s* each – the same price as a snipe – they had greatly decreased by 1825 and were almost extinct 25 years later. This may have been partly due to their vulnerability to hard winters, since they were apparently reluctant to migrate from the fens when a prolonged freeze-up prevented them from securing eels or other prey.

Young herons were also much esteemed: 'We have Heronies in England . . . in which Herons are so well instructed and accustomed to breed, that the owners make yearly a good profit of the young.'

But the primary reason for concern, as Harrison had noted in his reference to King John, was the adverse effect that a scarcity of wild-fowl would have on the major sport of that age – falconry. Herons were a favourite quarry of the falconer and, as royal game, were indeed entirely protected in Scotland for a period of three years from 1493 under penalty of a fine of £10 Scots. According to D. H. Madden, in *The Diary of Master William Silence*, hawking for herons began early in the spring when, towards the end of February, or early in March, they began to 'make their passage':

> It is then their custom to sally forth in the morning to distant rivers and ponds in search of food. Towards evening they leave their feeding grounds, and return to the heronry. The falconer stations himself in the open country, down-wind of the heronry, and as the bird flies over him on its homeward way, the falcons are cast off, and the flight begins.

A fearful toll of the duck in the fenlands from Essex to Yorkshire was also taken by decoys during the summer months. The use of decoys is reputed to date back to King John's reign. There was certainly litigation concerning their use at the end of the thirteenth century and again in the fifteenth when, in 1432, a mob armed with swords and sticks seized six hundred wildfowl out of the Abbot's decoy at Crowland Monastery in Lincolnshire. These decoys consisted of a V-shaped tunnel-net at the narrow end of a mere, flanked on either side by long nets, towards which the flappers and moulting adults were flushed from the marsh and reed-beds and driven into the tunnel by men and fleets of as many as four hundred small boats. Since three or four thousand duck could be decoyed in a single drive, slaughter on this scale ultimately resulted in duck driving being banned from May to August under the Act of 1534. Although this section of the Act was repealed seventeen years later, driving appears subsequently to have been conducted on only a small scale by owners of land until the eighteenth century.

Since the fenmen were no longer allowed to *drive* ducks during the summer months, the alternative was to *entice* them into decoy nets during the winter months. The prototype of these true decoys – derived from the *endekooy* of the Dutch, who were the originators of this form of wildfowling – appears to have been built early in the seventeenth century, and the first description of them is to be found in John Evelyn's *Diary*, in which he mentions the construction of one for Charles II in St James's Park, of all places, in 1665. The perennial winter flooding of great tracts of the Fens, prior to the completion in 1653 of the Dutch drainage programme, would in any case have prevented the use of this type of decoy at an earlier date. We are indebted to the parson-naturalist Richard Lubbock, writing in the 1840s, for the first accurate description of one:

> A decoy is a sequestered pool, with curving ditches, and of the depth of sixteen or eighteen inches of water in them, dug from the main water and covered with a net . . . These pipes or ditches, at their juncture with the main pool, are seventeen or eighteen feet across; the first hoop of netting, which is seven or eight yards up the pipe, is about ten feet in height; the hoops on which the netting is supported diminish in size gradually, and the purse net, into which the fowl are driven, is not of greater diameter than a common bow-net for pike. The reed fences must be about five feet and a half high, so that a moderate man, with a little care, is concealed behind them . . . The pipe measured on the curve is seventy-five yards, or thereabouts, and the reed screens are eleven, twelve or thirteen in number, each about twelve or thirteen feet in length. . . The aperture over which the dog leaps is about four feet wide . . .
>
> A decoy . . . should be sheltered on all sides by thicket and reed . . . It should bear with its pipes some resemblance to a gigantic spider with extended legs . . . These pipes should be disposed to suit different winds; for the most advantageous time to endeavour to lure fowl up a pipe is when the wind sets nearly from the apex of the pipe, where the purse net is placed, into the pool.

The decoy's effectiveness depended upon four factors. The first, skilful baiting of the water leading to the tunnel with such feed as oats and buckwheat sprinkled with hempseed oil, or maltings flavoured with aniseeed. The second, the use of decoy ducks, preferably dark grey and loud quackers: 'They well know their work, and when the drives took place would go on quietly swimming about as if nothing had happened.' The third, exciting the curiosity of the wild ducks with a dog which, by showing itself at intervals, attracted the duck further and further up the tunnel. The decoy dog, or even ferret, was usually reddish or liver-coloured and therefore perhaps more conspicuous or resembling a fox. And the fourth factor was the decoy-man himself who, when the duck had swum far enough up the tunnel, appeared at the critical moment and frightened them into the purse-net at the head of the tunnel. One might add that according to one decoy-man: 'A piece of burning turf was an essential, the nose of the duck being so acute.'

According to Lubbock, the decoy-man visited his pipes about one or two in the afternoon and, unseen, made his observations from behind the reed screen:

> Should he see the banks at the entrance of a pipe well lined with fowl . . . he looks out for a decoy duck or two . . . If any are in sight, probably they will come in expectation of barley as soon as

45. A Duck Decoy

the dog is put round; but should they be out of ken, the slightest whistle will command their attention, and . . . they will probably bring more or less of the wild-fowl to the entrance of the pipe – they seldom persuade them to come further. The decoy-man, posting himself at one of the screens nearest the pool, flings a mouthful of bread, which the dog does not directly pick up, but performs a circumbendibus, jumping over at the opening before him, and returning to his master at the next: thus appearing to the fowl for a moment, and then vanishing. If they follow the deceiver, the dog is worked at the next screen, going up the pipe, and the decoy-man runs him around, quicker or slower, according to the motions of the fowl, which he can see by peeping through the reed screen . . . Should all go right, and the fowl work well, when they have ascended the pipe far enough . . . the decoy-man turns back and displays his hat behind them; a confused skurry then takes place, all striving to be first into the fatal purse net.

During the eighteenth and nineteenth centuries as many as a hundred of these decoys were catching duck in the eastern counties alone, especially Lincolnshire, and there were numbers of smaller ones in other parts of England, including a dozen in the vast morasses around

Glastonbury, and also in Ireland; and since a single decoy-man and his dog could catch between five and twelve thousand duck – predominantly mallard, wigeon and teal – during the course of one winter, the total annual toll of duck in Britain must have been of the order of half a million.

During these centuries too, and particularly towards the end of the nineteenth, there were further major drainage projects and extensive reclamation of marshland for agricultural purposes. In 1824 a writer to the Norfolk and Norwich Naturalists' Society recalled that in earlier days: 'Such was the difficulty in getting from place to place in winter, that when a carriage was used, bundles of coarse herbage had to be carried for placing in the wheel ruts'; while Lubbock, writing in 1847, stated that:

> Since I first began to sport, about 1816, a marvellous alteration has taken place in Norfolk, particularly in the marshy parts. When first I remember our fens they were full of Terns, Ruffs, and Red-legs . . . Now, these very parts, which were the best . . . are totally drained.

So, too, about 1875 another Norfolk naturalist, Thomas Southwell, was lamenting that 'The wavy swell of the soughing reeds has given place to the bending ears of golden corn; and the boom of the Bittern, the scream of the Godwit, and the graceful flight of the glancing Tern, are sounds and sights altogether of the past.'

The drainage of Whittlesey Mere in 1851 almost completed the obliteration of some 680,000 acres of fenland, leaving only fragments totalling a few thousand acres; and between 1800 and 1850 a combination of land reclamation, cheap firearms and rapid rail transport, together with the demands of gourmands and the activities of private and commercial collectors who paid high prices for birds and their eggs, wiped out six species of birds and decimated a dozen more.

The wild grey lag geese were probably the first of the six species to be exterminated, for there is no further mention of them after 1768 when Pennant stated that they were resident in the Fens throughout the year, breeding in them and hatching about eight or nine young. The lack of any detailed accounts of the grey lags, which must formerly have bred in some numbers in the eastern counties of England and Scotland, is mystifying. That they were regarded as a typical English bird is implied by some lines from two old songs quoted by Brian Vesey-Fitzgerald in his *British Game:*

> What of the shaft?
> The shaft was cut in England,
> A long shaft, a strong shaft,
> Barbed and trim and true.
> So we'll drink all together
> To the grey goose feather
> And the land where the grey goose flew.

Oh where be those bold Spaniards to make so brave a boast oh!
They shall eat the grey goose feathers, but we shall eat the roast oh!

Were the grey lags so common as not to be noteworthy, and regarded as adjuncts to the immense herds of their domestic descendants? At any rate, as breeding birds they were banished to the Highlands where, as Robert Gray described in 1871, in *The Birds of the West of Scotland*, they nested in considerable numbers in the Outer Hebrides:

> For the last hundred years . . . the flocks of wild geese . . . have been kept at bay by fires alone. As soon as the breeding season is over the geese gather into large flocks, and are then very destructive to farm produce of all kinds . . . Several fires are made in the fields, and kept burning night and day; by this means the crops are to a great extent saved; but the moment any of the fires are allowed to fail, the geese, which are constantly shifting about on the wing, suddenly pitch on the uprotected spot.

By 1939, however, they had almost been exterminated in the Highlands too, though during the post-war years their numbers have been boosted by protection and the introduction of stock from northern Europe.

The next species to become extinct in the Fens was the avocet, which survived until the 1820s, and for another twenty years in the Humber. In addition to the hazards presented by the destruction of their habitat and harassment by collectors, the avocets were also persecuted by anglers who coveted their feathers for dressing flies, while according to Southwell: 'At the beginning of the present century the poor people of Salthouse made their "puddings and pancakes" of the eggs of this bird', and 'the gunners to unload their punt guns, would sometimes kill ten or twelve at a shot.'

Black-tailed godwit, which at one time had been very common in the Fens and also in the marshes of Norfolk and east Yorkshire, existed until the early 1830s, despite being 'accounted the daintiest dish in England'. They may have been particularly affected by the reclamation of the marshes because they are reported to require a special wetland habitat in which the water-table lies within four inches of the surface, for if the ground hardens out too much as the result of drainage, they are unable to probe for worms with their soft beaks, with the result that newly hatched young are liable to starve. It must be said, however, that on the breeding grounds these godwit appear to feed mainly on insects, which are also fed to the young ones.

It was in 1588 that a Yorkshireman, Richard Stanne, had noted down in his diary probably the first description of ruffs:

There was taken at Crowley in Lincolnshire in the winter 5 strange

46. A Ruff

> fowles of divers colours, having about their necks as it were great monstrous ruffs and had underneath these ruffs certaine quills to beare up the same in such a manner as our gallant dames have now of wier to beare up their ruffs . . About their heads they had feathers so curiously set together and frisled, altogeather like unto our nice gentlewomen who curle and frisle their haire about their heads.

But ruffs were also extensively exploited as table-birds, and the lengths to which gourmands were prepared to go to obtain such delicacies were described by George Montagu in a passage in his *Ornithological Dictionary,* which also stressed the toll taken of the various species of wading birds breeding in the marshes, although in the case of the ruffs the pursuit of these was restricted to a very few families of marshmen:

> Mr Towns, the noted feeder at Spalding assures us his family had been a hundred years in the trade . . . He undertook, at the desire of the late Marquis of Townsend, when that nobleman was Lord Lieutenant of Ireland [from 1767], to take some Ruffs to that

country, and actually set off with twenty-seven dozen from Lincolnshire, left seven dozen at . . .Chatsworth, continued his route across the Kingdom to Holyhead, and delivered seventeen dozen alive in Dublin, having lost only three dozen in so long a journey, confined and greatly crowded as they were in baskets, which were carried upon two horses.

Exploitation on this scale, together with the drainage of their habitat, resulted in the extermination of the ruffs shortly after the middle of the nineteenth century, though sporadic attempts to breed were made during the remainder of the century and also in 1907 and 1922.

Other species to become extinct in the Fens during the nineteenth century were Savi's warblers and the black terns. Turner had described the terns as constantly on the wing searching for prey, nesting in dense reed-beds, and so noisy during the breeding season as almost to deafen people living near lakes and fens. Persecution and the drainage of the carrs had terminated their occupation of the Fens by 1858, as persecution almost did that of the great crested grebe. In 1845 Lubbock had written of the latter:

> It will not happen in our time, but perhaps the next generation may speak of this bird as we now do of the Bustard, in the past tense. It is sometimes shot for the sake of the feathers, sometimes as pernicious to fish. The egges are always taken when found.

In 1851 indeed no fewer than 29 great crested grebes in full breeding plumage were killed in Norfolk by one man, and ten years later egg-taking and the fashion trade had almost exterminated them. However, after the passing of the Sea Birds Preservation Act in 1869 they steadily increased in numbers, and the proliferation of reservoirs and gravel-pits since the last war has boosted their population in various parts of Britain to their present total of more than 4,500 pairs.

There were also kites in the Fens, quartering the marshes for dead or wounded duck, and Browne watched the 'balbarshard' stooping at the huge flocks of coots on the Norfolk meres:

> Upon the appearance of a kite or buzzard I have seen them unite from all parts of the shoare in strange numbers when if the kite stoopes neare them they will fling up [and] spread such a flash of water up with their wings that they will endanger the kite . . . & so keepe him of agayne in open opposition. & in handsome provision they make about their nest agaynst the same bird of praye by bending and twyning the rushes and reeds so about them that they cannot stoope at their young ones or the damme while she setteth.

Although this behaviour on the part of the coots was never recorded again in Britain – nor that of safeguarding their nests – the authenticity of the observations was confirmed two hundred years later in Epirus and also in Africa.

But the Fens' characteristic birds of prey were the marsh harriers. Until the end of the seventeenth century they were very common not only in the Fens but also in the Irish bogs and reed-beds; and even in Lubbock's day almost every pool of any extent had a pair of 'moor buzzards' beating for hours at a time round and round the reeds that skirted the water, pouncing on any birds winged by sportsmen. But they (like the Montagu's harriers) were on the fringe of their European range in Britain. With the progressive and continuous destruction of their special marsh habitat, they have bred only sporadically in these islands during the past hundred years and more, and their breeding population has never exceeded twenty pairs in any one year.

After this long tally of disaster it is pleasant to be able to record the remarkable success of the Royal Society for the Protection of Birds in attracting some of these lost species back to Britain – presumably,

47. An Avocet

in the case of the waders, from surplus stocks on the Dutch pōlders. This success has been achieved by protection and, equally important, the provision of a suitable environment: a combination employed by local natural history societies to enable other species to repopulate former haunts. It will be recalled that bitterns had become virtually extinct by the middle of last century, though a single young one was in fact killed in Norfolk in 1886; but as early as 1900 they had begun to boom again almost every spring in the Broads and in 1911 a pair reared young. With the creation of new reed-bed habitats in such places as Minsmere in Suffolk, which had originally been flooded as a defence measure during the last war, and at Leighton Moss in Lancashire, bitterns have increased in numbers and colonised other parts of Britain. Similarly avocets were finally re-established as a British-breeding species in 1947, after an absence of more than 120 years, and thrived to such an extent in the special habitats at Havergate Isle and Minsmere that by 1971 some 134 pairs were nesting in Suffolk. Conditions in the Ouse Washes have also proved attractive to ruffs – after unsuccessful attempts to re-introduce them to the Fens in 1939 and 1957 – and 21 pairs nested on the Washes in 1971. In that year too 65 pairs of black-tailed godwit bred on the Washes, and they have also colonised several other localities from Kent to the Shetlands; while the two pairs of black terns that nested in the Washes in 1966 were the first to do so in Britain for more than eighty years, since earlier reports of their nesting at Pett Level in Sussex proved to be incorrect. In 1960 a small colony of Savi's warblers settled in Kent, and have since spread to a number of other counties. If this warbler can rehabilitate itself in Britain, why not others such as aquatic and melodious warblers, which may once have bred in this country?

Perhaps the most heartening and significant aspect of these successes was expressed by James Fisher in his *Birds as Animals:* 'For the first time in history man is able, to a certain extent, by protection, administration and care, to direct and improve the composition of his native bird fauna.'

21 Natives and Aliens in the Fens

Although the formation of peat in that part of the Fens known as the Broads had begun between 7500 and 5000 BP, it was the peat-cutters from the twelfth to the fourteenth centuries who were mainly responsible for creating the gigantic excavations represented by the 2,600 acres of the present-day Broads, as they sliced down through the successive layers of peat that had previously filled the valleys; but by the fifteenth century, after they had removed possibly 900 million cubic feet of peat, their cuttings had probably been replaced by open water and fens. Subsequently the waterways were kept open by regular mowing of the extensive and dense stands of reeds and sedge, which were used for thatching, kindling, litter, fodder and a variety of agricultural and household purposes.

Flooding has ever been a major, if sporadic, hazard for the fauna of the low-lying Fens, some of whose fresh-water lakes and waterways are located below sea-level. Were it not for the coastal defences, much inferior though these are to those protecting the Dutch pōlders, the Broads in particular and many thousands of acres of adjacent marshes would be at the mercy of regular flooding by the sea at that critical juncture when a north-easterly gale coincides with a high tide at the new or full moon. The earliest recorded inrush of the sea occurred in 1287, when several scores of people were drowned in one Broadland village, and there have been upwards of a dozen memorable inrushes since, with the sea surging twenty miles inland and thousands of acres remaining under salt water for periods of months. Such flooding may kill all fresh-water fish except eels, which are tolerant of both fresh and salt water, and prohibit breeding by bitterns, duck, waders, grebes, moorhens, coots and rails, while bearded tits, instead of nesting, collect together in flocks on tall reeds, which is normally a winter habit.

Although so fragmented and boat-congested during the summer season, the Broads can still lay claim to being a wilderness, palisaded with reeds and sprinkled with lilies, whose enormous root-stocks, up to nine feet long and two inches thick, growing longitudinally on the surface of the mud, present problems of removal from narrow channels; and the rank, bushy and sedgy fens backing the Broads still have a primeval appearance, though much of the marshy hinterland has been embanked and drained to form vast green cattle pastures. This modernisation has had its effect on the wildlife of the region. Moreover, a decline in the market for reeds and sedge since the First World War, and the consequent diminution in the area cut, has also resulted in large tracts reverting from open fen to dense bush or carr and scrub woodland. This has proved detrimental to such specialised inhabitants as marsh harriers, bearded tits and swallowtail butterflies.

Reedlings

Bearded tits – or more appropriately reedlings, since they are not true tits – are confined to large reed-beds throughout their vast though discontinuous range from East Anglia and eastern Spain to Lake Khoma near Vladivostok on the Pacific coast. Since the great majority are sedentary in their reed-beds all through the year, their survival is always at risk, for in addition to the hazard of the reed-beds being submerged by floods, they appear to be vulnerable to certain conditions prevailing in some severe winters, and on several occasions have been almost exterminated in Britain and central Europe. Indeed after the 1947 blizzards only a single bird – a male – may have survived in the whole of Norfolk, together with a very few pairs in Suffolk. However, since 1959 the reedlings have benefited from a series of favourable winters and, because they have always tended to wander locally during the autumn and winter, have dispersed to other localities in Britain, as far west as Dorset and as far north as Lincolnshire, in which they were previously unknown or had rarely visited. The precise cause of their vulnerability to hard winters is debatable. It is usually asserted that while during the summer months they feed largely on small insects and beetles picked off the reed stems, in winter they do so mainly on the seeds of reeds and reed-mace – the false bullrush; but if heavy snowfalls or freezing fog cakes the reed litter with ice they cannot obtain the seeds, and therefore starve: whereas in more severe winters, but without freezing fog, the seeds remain accessible. However, two of the most knowledgeable of Broadland naturalists, E.L. Turner and Anthony Buxton, doubted whether in fact the reedlings ever ate seeds in winter. According to Emma Turner, their principal food at this season consisted of two kinds of larvae, one of which bores into reed stems and the other into the reed-mace, causing the 'pokers' of the latter to burst out and become fluffy. In her experience it was largely owing to the presence of these grubs that the frail reedlings were able to endure the rigours of a Broadland winter, since, with these available, they did not have to venture out of the shelter of the reed-beds, and indeed flocked to those areas where reeds were being cut for thatching purposes and the grubs were easier to obtain.

In addition to natural hazards, the reedlings have had, like other fen birds, to contend with the avarice of collectors. During the latter half of the nineteenth century they became increasingly scarce owing to dealers' demands for both birds and eggs – one dealer receiving 113 eggs in two weeks – and by 1898 only 33 pairs remained in Norfolk. However, by 1909, with the aid of protection, the Broadland population had begun to increase again and, despite being decimated during the hard winters of 1916-17 and 1947, had risen to 400 pairs by 1972, aided by the immigration of Dutch birds from the vast tracts of reedbeds produced by land reclamation in the Ijsselmeer.

Butterflies

Birds were not the only Fenland fauna to become extinct as a result of the activities of collectors and the loss of habitat due to drainage and other factors. That the swallowtail butterfly is still at least as abundant in Broadland as before the first war, is – as E.A. Ellis has pointed out – because considerable tracts of watery fens which used to be mown regularly in summer, and occasionally burnt off in early spring, have been left to grow wild during the past thirty years or so. In these places, the main food plant in Britain, though not in Europe, of the swallowtail's caterpillars, the milk parsley – also peculiar to the Broads

8. A Swallowtail Butterfly

– has flourished and the larvae and pupae have not been disturbed: whereas at Wicken Fen in Cambridgeshire swallowtails have now become extinct, following upon temporary cultivation of a part of the conservation area.

A rather similar case is that of the large copper butterfly, which was first reported from Huntingdonshire fens in 1759. It was extremely common in the 1820s, and in 1843 pupae from the Wood Walton fen could be bought for 4*d* a dozen; yet within the next four to eight years the large coppers had been exterminated in their last haunts of Holme Fen and Whittlesey Mere by a combination of draining, mowing and burning, by floods, and in the final stage, when they had become very localised, by over-collecting of both caterpillars and mature insects. The large copper's life cycle is inextricably linked with its caterpillars' food plant, the great water dock; but the female is selective in her choice of docks on which to lay her eggs, preferring those growing away from the water's edge, though these are not as tall and leafy as those at the edge and are also liable to die off prematurely. Whether the protection of ants, which lick a sweet secretion exuded by the caterpillar's skin, is also an essential factor in the copper's choice of habitat, as in the case of the blue butterflies, is not known.

Various attempts have been made to re-establish large coppers in the Fens. In 1909 a smaller and less brilliantly coloured race – *Lycaena dispar rutilus*, which inhabits a large part of Europe – was introduced to Wicken Fen. However, *rutilus* differs from the British copper, *L. dispar dispar,* in feeding on more than one variety of plant (and also in being double-brooded), and was apparently unable to adapt to the scarcity of water docks at Wicken, and none survived. Then in 1913 great water docks were planted in a Tipperary bog in Ireland, and the following year a thousand *L.d. rutilus* were imported there from marshes north of Berlin. With these a colony was established in Tipperary, and in 1926 more than five hundred insects from this stock were liberated at a site in Norfolk, but with no success. In the meantime in 1915 scattered pockets of another race, *L.d. batavus,* almost identical to the lost British race, had been discovered in abandoned peat cuttings in Friesland; and in 1927, after large quantities of great water dock had been planted at Wood Walton Fen, 25 male and 13 female *L.d. batavus* were released there. Despite sixty days of floods during their first winter the caterpillars survived, for when hibernating they can exist for long periods under several feet of water, and an apparently permanent colony was established; but in 1969 floods did in fact drown all the caterpillars in this colony, though it was successfully restocked four years later. Other unsuccessful attempts at re-introduction have also been made at Cambridge and in the Yare valley where, however, floods drowned the caterpillars, birds killed the butterflies, and coypus destroyed the water docks by gnawing their rootstocks in winter. Since 1879 a number of moths – including the reed tussock, the gypsy, the orache, the marsh dagger, the many-lined and the rosy marsh – have also become extinct in fen country, though the last-mentioned was rediscovered in west Wales in 1965.

Coypus

After some forty years of existence in the wild state in Britain, the coypu must, like the mink, be accepted as a permanent member of the British fauna, though originating as an escape from fur farms in the thirties. A massive dark-brown rodent with a scaly rat-like tail, the coypu reaches a length of 3½ feet and may weigh as much as fifty pounds. It is properly an inhabitant of swamps, marshes, rivers and lake shallows in South America, where because of its supposed similarity in appearance and habits to the otter – of which there are none in South America – it is known by its Spanish name of *nutria.* Coypus were subsequently introduced to North America, where they may have taken over niches left vacant by the decimation of the beavers.

By 1946 feral coypus had become well established in the English Broads and by the end of the fifties there were possibly 200,000 in East Anglia, for the toll taken of their young by such natural predators as otters, foxes, brown rats, stoats, owls, harriers, herons and bitterns was insignificant. Moreover, they not only began breeding when eight months old – though bearing small and infrequent litters up to the age of fifteen months – but did so at all seasons of the year and produced two or three litters of from three to as many as eleven, though commonly five, young annually. The latter were born on large platforms, resembling swans' nests, composed of reed and sedge with the addition in some cases of slender twigs which the adults cut with their very large orange-coloured incisor teeth from sallow or wild currant bushes. In grazing marshes, however, where there was little cover, the young were born in burrows excavated in the dyke banks. Born fully furred and with eyes open, the latter were precocious enough to take to the water and also feed on vegetable matter within 24 hours of birth, though the female continued to suckle them for seven or eight weeks.

Normally nocturnal, the coypus slept by day on small platforms in the reed-beds, in couches gnawed out of sedge tussocks, or in their bank burrows. Unlike musk-rats, they did not undermine river banks because their burrows were usually short – only about four feet long and eight or nine inches in diameter – though in some instances they penetrated the dyke bank from water level to ground level. Between dusk and dawn they trod out well-worn tracks from the waterside to their feeding places on the marshes, uttering mournful cries in the moonlight. However, in frosty weather they fed during the daytime, and on warm sunny days might disport in quiet backwaters, floating with their tails stiffly erect.

During their occupation of the Broads the coypus made what Ellis has described as a tremendous impact on the vegetation by their selective feeding, though they did perform one useful service in opening up overgrown banks and waterways by removing weed, and did not cause much damage during the earlier stages of their colonisation. Indeed, according to Ellis, by eating out reed-beds and thus greatly increasing the water area, the coypus converted large patches of fen into expanses of black mud and shallow water, studded with tufts of purple loosestrife, which formed new nesting habitats for black-headed gulls and common terns and excellent feeding places for duck and wading birds. But once the coypus became numerous in any locality they affected the indigenous fauna adversely by altering the environment. They burrowed extensively in the drained levels and flattened and destroyed much of the vegetational cover; they damaged harvestable reeds and sedge; they virtually destroyed pioneer communities of vegetation round many of the Broads since they fed mainly on marsh and water plants; and they browsed down sallow, willow and ozier bushes, and killed mature trees by barking. They also damaged crops and pasture, travelling long distances inland to these when the marshes were frozen, and by 1961 the threat to the Broadland ecology had become so serious that a massive trapping campaign was launched. This resulted in the destruction of 100,000 coypus during the next two years; and their numbers were reduced to a controllable minimum during the severe winter of 1962-3, when for three months all dykes, broads and several miles of river were frozen over, compelling the coypus to remain above ground throughout this period, when many of those young born in January and February died as a result of eating frozen vegetation – as did some of the adults. During the past decade, however, their numbers have again increased to about 7,000, though they have not extended their range.

Musk-Rats

A much more harmful escape in the late 1920s from fur farms in various parts of Britain, but not the Broads, was the musk-rat – the musquash of the Cree Indians and the predominant mammal of marshes and slow-flowing rivers over almost all of North America, where it coexists peaceably with the introduced coypus. Primarily vegetarians, the musk-rats' preferred food consists of reeds and bullrushes. These they cut with their sharp incisors into manageable five- or ten-inch sections, which are either eaten *in situ* or more usually carried to burrows in the banks or to little floating shelters, pyramidal in shape and composed mainly of bullrushes and supported on a raft of their stems. In shallow marshes, liable to be submerged by flooding, musk-rats usually build dome-shaped lodges of vegetable fibres, grass stems, bullrushes and a few sticks, as alternative residences to their bank burrows. To avoid flooding, however, river-dwelling musk-rats are obliged to engineer extensive series of bank burrows, which may be constructed in systems of superimposed galleries up to eighty feet long and all inter-connected, with as many as half a dozen entrances, often several feet below the water-level. They may even tunnel under a stream from one bank to the other. In their North American environment of extensive marshes and large river systems these excavations do not result in much damage, but within the limited confines of heavily populated Britain and Europe, where lodges were built only as winter shelters in marshland and burrowing was widespread, banks and dams were undermined, riverside trees collapsed into the streams, and backwaters were choked with the fallen trees and drifting masses of vegetation.

Despite heavy predation on the musk-rats' young by brown rats and to a lesser extent by stoats, their extermination in Britain proved difficult, not only because of the complexity of their burrow systems, but also because of their prolific breeding. In America the female produces two or three litters of from seven to ten young, with the first litter in April or May; and when nine or ten months old the young ones are themselves in breeding condition. But in Britain the in general milder winters and greater abundance of food made it possible for the females to breed from February through to November, with the result that six or seven litters of eight young were being produced annually. Moreover, the young of the earlier litters, weaned when a month old, dispersed from their home range in the autumn, and those of the later litters the following spring, to colonise new localities and excavate new burrows within fifteen days of their departure. Thus, so rapid was their increase in Britain that in one Scottish district, in which five females and four males had escaped in 1927, 870 had been trapped by 1933; while in an Irish locality of 150 square miles, 487 were trapped during the one winter of 1933-4 – the progeny of a single pair of escapes in 1927. However, before the population of muskrats in Britain could build up to plague numbers anywhere near that of the estimated ten million in central Europe in 1935, the trapping campaign was successful in exterminating them by the end of 1937.

Mink

In America large numbers of musk-rats are killed by mink, though these cannot break into the rats' mud-hardened winter lodges. Potentially, the most destructive escape from fur farms in Britain has been that of the American mink. Though feeding mainly on crayfish and clams, and swimming well enough with their partially webbed feet to catch fish, they are the most rapacious of the weasels, the wolverine excepted, and have taken the place of the arctic fox as the principal menace to nesting wildfowl in Iceland since their colonisation of that island during the 1950s and 1960s. They have indeed been responsible for a marked decrease in a number of species of duck, and in some localities have compelled the harlequins to cease nesting on islands, and retreat to the safer havens of small brooks leading into the main rivers. Ironically, the European mink probably never reached Britain. But since 1957, when they were first recorded breeding in the wild state, feral American mink have dispersed over Britain from Cornwall to Inverness, and have

49. A Mink

also become established in Ireland; and it seems unlikely that further colonisation can be halted by any natural predator, since they are apparently living peaceably with polecats in Pembroke, Shropshire and Herefordshire, and the two species have always coexisted on the Continent.

22 Bustards Fatting Themselves with Ease and Eating

In this post-war era of conservation, which recognises that you are not likely to be successful in re-establishing a species by merely introducing stock from abroad and plonking it down in any old spot, but must first prepare a suitable environment, one of the more ambitious projects is to re-instate the splendid great bustard in Britain. An attempt to do so was made early this century when free-flying young were released on the Suffolk Brecks, but they dispersed and were shot. In 1970, however, a ten-acre field, which had never been ploughed or sprayed, was leased from the Chemical Defence Establishment at Porton Down. Though not actually a part of Salisbury Plain, the Establishment's four thousand acres of chalk grassland and scrub approximates to the natural habitat of bustards, and insects, essential as food for the young bustards, are abundant. The area also includes a tract of flints – probably excavated by rabbits and now holding possibly a dozen pairs of stone curlew – unique on the chalk hills of southern England and comparable to the Brecks. Disturbance in the Establishment's prohibited area, further concealed by upwards of three thousand acres of farmland and woods, is minimal.

There are now six hens and four cocks, imported from Portugal, in the ten-acre field, and they are provided with a regular grain supplement, in addition to mustard, rape and beans sown for food and also nesting cover; for though it is true that captive bustards have been observed to eat raw meat and mice, they do not, after sowing-time, feed on flesh, livers and young lambs – as Thomas Muffett would have us believe, according to his quaint book, *Health's Improvement*, published about 1595. Although hens breed when three years old, the cocks are not sexually mature until six. So, with the hens now five years old and the oldest cock seven, it remains to be seen whether young British-born bustards can be reared and survive under controlled conditions to repopulate such habitats as are left to them.

Despite their spectacular size and obvious edibility – and we know that the young ones were taken alive to be fattened for the table –

there do not appear to be any references to great bustards in Britain before 1371 when, according to the Chamberlain's accounts for the Borough of King's Lynn, '39*s*. 8*d*. was paid for wine, bustards, herons, and oats, presented to John Nevile, Admiral.'

Gesner asserted that they were exceedingly numerous, being killed by hawks and dogs – though probably mainly shot with crossbows – and their feathers used for dressing flies; but this can only have been the case in a limited number of localities. As early as 1534 bustards were, as we have seen, one of the beneficiaries of Henry VIII's first avian conservation law, under which their eggs were protected. In 1610 John Denton of Cardew described them as very scarce and only on Salisbury Plain, noting that they 'run as fast as a hare along ye ground, for a considerable time before they can take flight, and are very difficult to be taken; as they will seldom come with in a gun shot.' However, we know that there were also droves on the Sussex and Berkshire downs, the Brecklands of Norfolk and Suffolk, the heaths of Newmarket and Royston, and the wolds of Lincolnshire and the East Riding of Yorkshire. A hill figure of a bustard in Staffordshire suggests that they may have bred in that county too, while there is a tradition of them at Chillingham and, according to an inexplicable and unsubstantiated account by Boece, writing in 1526, there was a small drove in the Merse of Berwickshire:

> Merchia is also the breeding ground of Gustards, as they are commonly known, which are quite similar to partridges in their flesh and the colour of their plumage . . . This is an uncommon bird which normally shuns the sight of man. Its eggs are laid on the ground without any covering; should it find that they have been touched by man or even lightly imbued with the contagion of his breath . . . it immediately abandons them as being unsuitable for producing chicks and takes itself off elsewhere to lay more eggs.

The largest droves were in East Anglia and Wiltshire (whose county coat-of-arms includes a bustard as a support), and it was presumably on Salisbury Plain that Thomas Muffet observed that: 'In the Summer towards the ripening of the Corn, I have seen half-a-dozen of them in a wheat-field fatting themselves (as a Deer will doe) with ease and eating'; but we know almost nothing about the bustards' habits in Britain. In Norfolk, according to Stevenson, writing some thirty years after they had been exterminated, the frosts and snows of January usually brought them into the fields to feed on the turnip-tops. They remained in droves on the farmland until the late spring or early summer, when the cocks apparently left the hens. After the corn had been cut they gathered in droves again for a month or six weeks; but little was seen of either cocks or hens from about the middle of September until Christmas, during which period they presumably migrated to other feeding grounds.

50. A Great Bustard

Late in the seventeenth century Sir Thomas Browne had described the bustard as 'not infrequent in the champain and fieldie part' of Norfolk, where the largest drove of which there is a record numbered 27 birds; but though hens in this drove survived until 1838, no fertile eggs were laid after 1832. They were the last British bustards, for despite a summer close season being introduced on Salisbury Plain in 1775, when droves of more than 50 were still to be seen, and though Colonel Thornton was flying his hawks at them (unsuccessfully) in the early years of the next century, the Wiltshire bustards had been wiped out by 1820. The Suffolk drove of up to 40 birds had been exterminated by 1812, and the Yorkshire droves of up to 25 birds, located mainly near the coast at Scarborough, by about 1830. That hens greatly outnumbered cocks in the later stages may have accelerated their extinction. In France most of the droves were exterminated at about the same time as in Britain, though one very large group survived in Champagne, a hundred miles east of Paris, into the 1860s. In Denmark and southern Sweden bustards have been extinct for several centuries, and today they exist precariously in Portugal, Spain,.central Europe, Poland and Asia Minor.

In both Britain and France the annihilation of the bustards can be attributed to the perfecting of firearms, coupled with changes in agricultural practices. They were peculiarly vulnerable to the 'stalking-horse' approach, which wildfowlers in the Fens often used when duck-shooting, and which is still employed for bustards in Spain. Londoners would go down to Salisbury Plain to shoot bustards by driving round and round a drove in a cart in gradually diminishing circles; and a correspondent to *The Field* in 1878 recounts how:

51. A Great Bustard at it Nest

In my recent visit to the fens of Cambridgeshire, I met with some old warreners who recollected when the Bustard was common. They represented it as an extremely sagacious bird, and that therefore extraordinary pains were resorted to for that purpose. At Icklingham is still preserved one of the Bustard-fowler's 'Cribs'. This 'Crib' is a sort of rude cabin about three feet high, covered with furze and bramble. It moved upon four wheels; in its centre a windlass was fixed; and at different parts of the fen posts were firmly planted, attached to which were ropes having their connection with the windlass. The fowler, seated in the 'Crib', when he saw the Bustard alight and sufficiently engaged, would gradually wind the 'Crib' towards the direction of the bird, and when within shot, let fly.

On the Brecklands masked batteries of large duck-guns were sited to concentrate their fire on a spot strewn with turnips. Their triggers were attached to a cord perhaps half a mile long, and the shepherd and other farm labourers were instructed to pull this cord whenever they saw bustards within range.

But in Stevenson's opinion the bustards' 'chief destroyer was most assuredly the agriculturalist':

He found his plots wanted shelter, and planted long belts of trees to keep the wind from carrying his soil to the next parish . . . The effect of high winds, after dry weather in this district, is not easily described. The whole air is filled with sand, till it resembles a London fog. Nearly every particle of fertilizing matter is blown away from the land, as is shown for years afterwards by its barreness . . . The continuous drifting forward of innumerable sharp angular particles, consisting almost entirely of comminated flints, so chafes the tender cuticle of young corn or turnips, that an exposed breck after a few hours' gale, looks as if it had been exposed to a blast of air at an excessive temperature, and in a day or two the vegetation withers away . . . This intersecting of the open country was intolerable to the Bustard, which could not bear to be within reach of anything that might conceal an enemy. Its favourite haunts were, therefore, year by year restricted. But more than this, the substitution of wheat for rye, as the system of tillage improved, aimed a still more fatal blow at its existence. The hen Bustard almost always laid her eggs in the winter-corn. When this came to be wheat, it was still more an object to save as much [of the expensive seed] as possible, so the drill was invented. It was also worth while to keep the land well clear of weeds, and the horse-hoe, therefore, followed. This decided the Bustard's fate. Not a nest was there in the wheat-fields, but was either accidentally trodden down, or if seen in time . . . it was only that the eggs might be taken by the man or boy employed, and given to his master's wife, by whom they were set under a hen, or more commonly kept as 'curiosities'.

23 The Slaughter of the Birds of Prey

An Eagle for an Emperor
A Gerfalcon for a King
A Peregrine for an Earl
A Merlyon for a Lady
A Goshawk for a Yeoman
A Sparehawk for a Priest
A Muskyte* for 'an holiwater clerke'.

In some remote inter-glacial era gyr falcons were probably nesting on mountain crags in Britain, and rough-legged buzzards and snowy owls hunting over the tundra. Later, when dense forest replaced the tundra, there would have been goshawks and kites and perhaps eagle-owls, all of which are mentioned in the *Anglo-Saxon Chronicle*. In contrast to our raptor-starved age, birds of prey appear to have been extraordinarily numerous throughout Britain until comparatively recently, and Giraldus, with his customary aplomb, asserted of Ireland that: 'This country produces in greater numbers than any other hawks, falcons, and sparrow-hawks . . . Eagles are as numerous here as kites in other countries,' adding that: 'It is, however, a remarkable fact in the history of this tribe of birds, that their nests are not more numerous than they were many centuries ago; and although they have broods every year, their numbers do not increase.'

He also gave an accurate description of the osprey's fishing technique, though he adhered to the myth of an osprey having one foot clawed and the other webbed; while William Harrison stated that:

> We have also ospraies, which breed with us in parks and woods, whereby the Keepers of the same do reap in breeding time no small

*The male sparrow-hawk, inferior to the female for hawking.

commodity; for, so soon almost as the young are hatched, they tie them to the butt ends or ground ends of sundry trees, where the old ones finding them, do never cease to bring fish unto them, which the keepers take and eat from them.

From the middle of the twelfth century until the seventeenth birds of prey – especially peregrines, goshawks and sparrow-hawks – were strictly protected in Britain in the interests of falconry. Under Henry VII the penalty for taking the eggs of falcons, goshawks and lanners (peregrines) was imprisonment for a year and a day, while in Scotland numerous statutes for the protection of hawks date from as early as the latter half of the twelfth century. Falcons were of considerable value. The peregrines on Lundy had been famous since the thirteenth century when an inventory in 1274 noted that: 'There is also one eyrie of lanner falcons, which have sometimes three young ones, sometimes four . . . they build their nest in a place in which they cannot be taken.' But the most sought-after falcons inhabited the northern Highlands and Islands, and their eyries were often reserved by the original owners when grants of estate were made. James V paid £189 Scots to the Earl of Angus for a single falcon, and a pair were valued at £1,000 during the reign of his successor, who presented falcons from Caithness to the King of France, the Dauphin and the Duke of Guise.

Larks were hawked with merlins or hobbies, and the craze for falconry was such that, according to Sir John Sebright, hawking for magpies was far superior to any other kind:

A down or common, where low trees or thorn bushes are dispersed at the distance of from thirty to fifty yards apart, is the place best calculated for this diversion. When a Magpie is seen at a distance, a Hawk is immediately to be cast off. The Magpie will take refuge in a bush the moment that he sees the Falcon, and will remain there until the falconer arrives, with the Hawk waiting on in the air. The Magpie is to be driven from his retreat; and the Hawk, if at a good pitch, will stoop at him as he passes to another bush, from whence he is to be driven in the same way, another Hawk having previously been cast off, so that one or the other may always be so situated as to attack him to advantage. The second hawk is necessary, for the Magpie shifts with great cunning and dexterity to avoid the stoop; and when hard pressed, owing to the bushes being rather far apart, will pass under the bellies of the horses, flutter along a cart-track, and avail himself of every little inequality of the ground in order to escape. Four or five assistants, besides the falconer, who should attend solely to his Hawks, are required for this sport. They should be well mounted, and provided with whips; for the Magpie cannot be driven from a bush by a stick; but the crack of a whip will force him to leave it . . . It is not easy to take a Magpie in a hedge. Some must ride behind, and some before him; for unless compelled to

52. Golden Eagles at Their Eyrie

see over

> rise, by being surrounded on all sides, he will flutter along the hedge, so as to shelter himself from the Falcon.

However, other writers in the fourteenth and later centuries held different views about magpies, and in *A Cavalier's Note Book* we read that:

> If you take a quick and lively Magpie, and lay her on the ground upon her back in such sort that her wings be fastened to the earth, the stir and noise she will make will call many other Magpies about her, which alighting upon her (as it were to succour or relieve), she will hold the first that comes fast with her claws till you may come and take her. This you may pin down by the other in like manner, and so you may do until you have taken a great number of these birds. The best time for this is when they pair.

But in the seventeenth century the country gentleman's chief leisure pursuit of hawking gave way to fowling. Indeed, as early as 1718, when Giles Jacob published the *Compleat Sportman*, he could declare that he had ignored the diversion of hawking because it was so much disused in his time, 'especially since sportsmen are arrived at such perfection in shooting'. With the waning popularity of falconry the protection previously given to falcons and hawks was relaxed, and this marked the beginning of the decline in the numbers of birds of prey in Britain. The decline was accelerated by the Enclosures, by sheep farming and by the preservation of the sportsman's game on large estates, particularly in the Highlands, which entailed the extermination of all potential predators. Peregrines were now persecuted wherever possible, particularly on grouse moors, as were golden eagles, buzzards, hen-harriers and even ospreys. Yet a pair of the latter with young to feed required only eight or ten half-pound fish a day, and while some of these were the angler's trout, coarse fish were often preferred, especially pike which, basking near the surface, presented an easier target than trout. In four years in the 1830s no fewer than 310 hen-harriers were killed on a single Ayrshire estate, while the destruction of raptors from 1837-40 in Glen Garry was even more incredible, though some of the specific tallies are obviously questionable. However, during this period 1,795 birds of prey were slaughtered, in addition to 109 owls and 475 ravens. The raptors included 15 golden eagles and 27 sea eagles, 18 ospreys, 63 goshawks, 275 kites, 72 hen-harriers, 5 Montagu's harriers, 98 peregrines, 11 hobbies, 6 jerfalcons, 7 'orange-legged' falcons, 78 merlins, 462 kestrels, 285 buzzards, 371 rough-legged buzzards and 3 honey-buzzards. It is difficult to imagine what it must have been like to have been a naturalist in the Highlands in that century, when Osgood MacKenzie's stalker could kill ten golden eagles in two successive seasons and seven in each of another two years – or for that matter, in England, when in the 1830s buzzards, Montagu's and hen-harriers, kites, peregrines and also ravens were all nesting in the small Northumbrian parish of Eglingham.

Yet as early as the beginning of the present century George Bolam had been a good enough naturalist to realise that many of the grouse killed by peregrines – and these might amount to no more than one bird from every three hundred acres of moor – were wandering 'bachelors'. Today, two hundred years too late to prevent the slaughter of hundreds of thousands of raptors, field studies by the Unit of Grouse and Moorland Ecology based in Scotland have demonstrated that natural predation does not influence the fluctuations in the numbers of grouse, because the latter themselves regulate their density on a moor every spring and autumn by ejecting surplus stock. The predators, whether they be peregrines, eagles, hen-harriers, foxes or wild cats, prey almost exclusively on these surplus grouse. Thus although over a period of five years predators killed more than five hundred grouse in the study area, or about one-fifth of the total stock, this toll did not reduce the numbers of breeding grouse. Similar results were obtained during a five-year period on another moor. There, hen-harriers and foxes together accounted for six hundred grouse; but the bulk of these were surplus stock without territories, which would otherwise have succumbed to disease or starvation. Studies of goshawks and sparrow-hawks in Germany have also shown that their predation had no decisive or injurious effects on the breeding stock of game. By contrast, an epidemic of disease among wildfowl in Hungary was halted when all affected birds were killed by immigrant peregrines.

As early as 1457 James I of Scotland had ordered the destruction of buzzards, no doubt at the request of warreners concerned for their rabbits. In 1797 the *Encyclopaedia Britannica* pronounced the buzzard to be the 'most common of the hawk kind in England', not excepting kestrels and sparrow-hawks. Yet by the early nineteenth century this most harmless and beneficial of raptors, whose prey consisted of rabbits, rodents, beetles and carrion, had been exterminated in almost every part of Britain by gamekeepers. In East Anglia, however, a decline in the numbers of sheep, and therefore of carrion, may have been a contributing factor; and persecution cannot wholly account for its total extinction in Ireland from about 1890. But there must have been substantial breeding nuclei of buzzards here and there, for a relaxation of universal harassment during the two wars enabled them to recover without any special protection to a peak of perhaps twenty or thirty thousand. However, their numbers were again reduced locally by the decimation of their rabbit prey during the myxomatosis plague, though the scarcity of rabbits also had the beneficial effect of dispersing some buzzards into new localities, which resulted in the colonisation of some Scottish areas and the recolonisation of Ulster. Once again the indomitable buzzard succeeded in boosting its numbers to its present population of possibly fifteen or twenty thousand.

In addition to persecution by gamekeepers the raptors, as they became rarer, had also to contend with that by collectors. Although collections of birds and their eggs were being made in the later years of the seventeenth century, and no fewer than 57 private collectors provided Thomas Bewick with specimens for his woodcuts prior to 1830, it was in the nineteenth century that naturalists amassed huge stores of skins and eggs, obtained mainly from dealers and taxidermists, while natural history museums accumulated tens of thousands of specimens. Nor was it only the large and showy birds that were collected. Yarrell quotes a contributor to the *Magazine of Natural History* concerning the Dartford warbler:

> I have seen them by dozens skipping about the furze, lighting for a moment on the very point of the sprigs, and instantly diving out of sight again, singing out their angry impatient ditty . . . Mounted on a tall horse, and riding quietly along the outside, while the fox-hunters have been drawing the furze-fields, I have seen the tops of the furze quite alive with these birds.

But in 1868 we hear that 'a person in the neighbourhood' of Sunninghill 'obtains specimens at all times of the year, with which to supply the London bird-stuffers'; while five years later Gould stated that: 'All the commons south of London, from Blackheath and Wimbledon to the coast, were formerly tenanted by this little bird; but the increase in the numbers of collectors has, I fear, greatly thinned them in all districts near the metropolis.'

It was the excesses of the remorseless Victorians that finally led to the various preservation Acts passed between 1869 and 1896. In view of the enterprising persistence, effrontery, ruthlessness and commando-like hardihood of the gentlemen adventurers of that era – Charles St John, Lewis Dunbar and his brother William, Edward T. Booth, John Wolley, Roualeyn Gordon Cumming who subsequently shipped his guns to bigger game in Africa – it is surprising that rare raptors were able to survive as long as they did. At the end of May 1848 St John was hauling a boat over the hills of north-west Sutherland, where his old grey pony could not do so, in search of nesting ospreys, golden eagles, wild geese and black-throated divers:

> The eagles' nests had already been robbed by the shepherds, who have found out their value. We, however, procured six eagles' eggs, besides peregrine falcons'. A shepherd told us of an osprey's nest, or, as he called it, an 'eagle fisher', on an island in a loch . . . We started at daylight over bog and rock, dragging our boat with us, and on reaching the loch I was delighted beyond expression at seeing two ospreys, one of them on the nest, and the other soaring above, uttering cries of alarm at our approach.
>
> The nest was placed in a most curious situation. About a hundred and fifty yards from the shore there rose from the deep water a solitary rock about ten feet high, shaped like a broken sugar-loaf, or truncated cone; on the summit of this was the nest – a pile of sticks

53. Ospreys at Their Nest

of very great depth, evidently the accumulation of many breeding seasons. How this heap of sticks withstood the winter gales without being blown at once into the water, puzzled me.

By their activities in 1848 and 1849 St John, Wolley and William Dunbar succeeded in wiping out the Sutherland ospreys, which had half a dozen eyries in the north-west of the county, and on 29 June 1850 Dunbar wrote to Wolley:

> I do believe, at this moment, that there is only one Osprey's nest in this country, and that has been taken by Lord Grosvenor's keeper. I am afraid that Mr St John, yourself, and your humble servant, have finally done for the ospreys.

Yet paradoxically St John could write:

> I cannot say . . . that I am at all anxious to see our island entirely clear of what game preservers call 'vermin'. There is more beauty and more to interest one in the flight and habits of a pair of falcons than in a whole pack of grouse; and I regret to see how rare these birds, and eagles, and many others are daily becoming, under the influence of traps, poison, and guns.

In Britain ospreys selected three types of nest site – a conical rock at some distance from the shores of a loch, the summit of a tall pine or oak, or an isolated ruin. At the end of April 1851 Lewis Dunbar robbed the long-established eyrie on the low square tower of the ancient castle in Loch an Eilein at three o'clock in the morning, after walking nearly all night, probably from Grantown twenty miles distant, and reaching the loch in the middle of a snowstorm. He describes in his letters how, having tied a cord to his life-preserver, and leaving the other end in charge of a man on the shore, he swam out to the island, where he tied the rope to a stone and climbed up the ruins, slipping about in six inches of snow. Having found two eggs in the nest, he discovered that he had left his cap behind him. He tried carrying one egg in his mouth, but could not breathe with it; and finally he swam ashore on his back with an egg in each hand. He blew the eggs in the boathouse, washing out the inside with whisky.

On 8 May the following year he robbed the eyrie for the fifth time between eleven o'clock and midnight:

> As it was very dark and no moon, I had the precaution to take my cousin along with me . . . I took off my clothes and put on my life-preserver, attaching a cord to the back of it . . . I got over quite safe. The cock bird flew away before I reached the island; and after I had climbed up to the top of the ruin, and was just on the nest, I put out my hand to catch the hen, but when she felt me she gave a loud scream and flew away also. On arriving at the island I had fixed the cord to a bush; and on coming back I had some difficulty in finding it owing to the darkness of the night; but when I did so, I secured it to my belt and bawled to my cousin to pull, which he did. In the middle I was taken with cramp, but he succeeded in hauling me out. After dressing, we forded the river, which was very high at the time; and on going across with my cousin on my way back, I stumbled, and down he went, but he managed to get to his feet, and this put an end to our adventures.

Between 1848 and 1852 the Loch an Eilein eyrie was robbed six times and the neighbouring Loch Morlich eyrie four times or more, and no young ospreys were reared in Strathspey from 1880 to 1894. By the beginning of the present century ospreys had virtually ceased to breed in Britain, though a single bird continued to frequent an eyrie at Loch Arkaig in Inverness-shire until 1908, and a pair actually bred at Loch Loyne, also in Inverness-shire, in 1916. How remarkable it is that, after an absence of so many years, a pair of ospreys should have returned in the 1950s to nest at Loch Garten, ten miles from Loch an Eilein. Since then other localities in the Highlands have been occupied and the ospreys have been so successful, mainly because of round-the-clock protection throughout the breeding season, that in 1972 twelve young were reared at six eyries. Recoveries of ringed birds, mainly immature, indicate that most of those visiting Britain, presumably while on passage between Scandinavia and Africa, come from Sweden. Are these the recolonisers of the Highlands?

But let us review the fortunes – or, rather, misfortunes – of other birds of prey, which by 1900 had reached their nadir.

In the 1660s John Ray, who has been termed the greatest field naturalist of all time, had accurately described the nesting habits of the honey-buzzard:

> It builds its nest of small twigs, laying them upon wool and upon the wool its eggs. We saw one that made use of an old kite's nest to breed in, and fed its young with the nymphae of wasps: for in the nest we found the combs of wasps' nests and in the stomachs of the young the limbs and fragments of wasp-maggots. There were in the nest only two young ones, covered with a white down, spotted with black. Their feet were of a pale yellow, their bills between the nostrils and the head white. Their craws large, in which were Lizards, Frogs etc. . . . This bird runs very swiftly like a Hen.

Although several pairs of honey-buzzards probably always survived in the New Forest, together with the odd pair on the Welsh marches, they were among the first raptors to be brought near to extinction, with upwards of £40 being paid for one pair with nestlings. But persecution has not been entirely responsible for their present rarity, since their peculiar diet of wasp and bee grubs – of which a pair with young possibly consume 250 a day – requires the special climatic conditions of warm summers with moderate rainfall, coupled with the special habitat of large tracts of mixed woodlands with open glades; and the latter become ever sparser in this country.

The number of hobbies in Britain must also be limited under modern conditions by their specialised requirements of low-altitude heathland – in which they can hawk for their main prey, insects, and for such small birds as larks – associated with mixed woodlands that preferably include pines in which they can breed in the old nests of crows or in the old dreys of squirrels; and their present population of perhaps 50 or 75 pairs may be the maximum practicable in a twentieth-century environment.

Since the territory of a breeding pair of goshawks extends to eight or twelve thousand acres of forest, usually coniferous, adjacent to open country, we do not need to look further than the wholesale destruction of forest for a major reason for their decline in Britain. There are indeed very few authentic records of their nesting. Colonel Thornton was presented with a young goshawk from Rothiemurchus in the 1780s, and stated that he saw some nests in the pine woods there and in Glen More, and a hundred years later a pair nested in a Perthshire forest; but instances of breeding in England are more likely to have been by escapes from falconers or by birds introduced by the latter

54. A Sea Eagle in Flight
55. A Golden Eagle in Flight
see over

than by genuinely wild birds, for from the earliest times falconers had allowed their goshawks to fly wild at the end of the hawking season late in March or early in April – a practice referred to as far back as Aelfric's *Colloquium* and again in the fifteenth-century *Paston Letters*. However, it is possible that the Forestry Commission's extensive conifer plantings may eventually attract wild goshawks.

The sanctuary of these vole-harbouring plantations, combined with less persecution in the Highlands and long-term protection in Orkney, certainly enabled hen-harriers to make a remarkable recovery from near-extinction in the 1940s to their present population of considerably more than a hundred pairs, and possibly two or three times that number; but although Montagu's harriers have also taken advantage of the new plantations, this has not resulted in them maintaining a stable presence in Britain – perhaps because they cease to nest when the growing cover becomes too dense – and their breeding population fluctuates between half a dozen and fifty pairs.

In 1688 a pair of golden eagles were still nesting in wooded country near Derwent in the Peak district, and eagles continued to breed at Martindale in the Lakes until 1789. Gamekeepers were not responsible for banishing eagles from the fells, but the sheep-farmers and shepherds. Today we know that most lambs allegedly killed by eagles are in fact taken as carrion when dead, and that lamb-killing in the central Highlands, for instance, occurs only in those localities in which the eagles' natural prey has been drastically reduced. At the outset the spread of sheep-farming in the western Highlands from the late eighteenth century boosted the eagle population because of the additional food supplies it provided in the form of carrion; and at the present time there is as dense a population of golden eagles in the island of Lewis as anywhere else in the Highlands because of the plentiful supply of carrion resulting from heavy mortality among the sheep stock. By contrast in the southern Cairngorms, where the standard of sheep-farming is higher, and where there are also extensive deer forests and grouse moors, 60 per cent of the dozen pairs of eagles' food comprises grouse and ptarmigan and 20 or 30 per cent blue hares and rabbits.

The last eyrie of sea eagles on the Isle of Wight was robbed in 1780, and by the end of that century these eagles had ceased to nest in the Lakes or anywhere else in England. Nevertheless, in the middle of the next century they were described as more numerous than golden eagles in Scotland. The numbers of the latter must always be limited because each pair requires between eleven and thirteen thousand acres of hunting territory over moor and hill; whereas the majority of sea eagles' eyries were on sea cliffs, though some were sited, like ospreys', on islands in lochs as far as ten miles from the sea. In *Ootheca Wolleyana* John Wolley described two islets in a Sutherland loch in the 1850s:

> In each were two or three little trees, and in each was a huge nest of the Sea-Eagle, fixed so near the ground that a child could see into it

– one nest some years old, the other repaired that season. Hooded crows built in the branches over the newer nest, and in spite of the frequent visits of the Eagles, a Wild Duck had its eggs not many yards off, and Geese bred there regularly. The other islet had been burnt several years before to dislodge a fox, and now its bright young heather again formed an excellent cover. A pair of Black-throated Divers crying on the surface of the loch, two wild Geese flying round and round, and an old Eagle with its broad white tail slowly wafting its way between me and the neighbouring mountain.

Sea eagles were still commoner than golden eagles in the western Highlands in the 1860s, when 57 were killed on a single estate in Skye in nine years and 52 on another estate in Wester Ross in twelve years. They, too, were universally persecuted by sheep-farmers and shepherds because of their alleged toll of new-born lambs. According to Prideaux Selby, no fewer than 171 were killed in Sutherland in three years in the 1830s, after the Commissioners of Supply, who were associated with sheep-breeding, had offered a bounty of three shillings for every eagle – a measure that no doubt inflated the actual number killed; and in *A Tour through Orkney and Shetland in 1774* George Low described how the half-dozen pairs of great skuas breeding on Foula were protected by the crofters because they drove the sea eagles and ravens off the hill and therefore away from the lambs:

> In Foula there is a privileged bird, no man will dare shoot it, under the penalty of 16*s*. 8*d*., nor destroy its eggs; when they meet it at sea, whatever fish they may have in the boat Skua always gets a share, and all this out of gratitude for beating off the Eagle, who does not venture to prey on the island during the whole course of the breeding season . . . Skua is not so strong as the eagle, but much more nimble; strikes at him without mercy, with such effect that he makes the other scream aloud, and his retreat is so sudden as to avoid all danger from the Eagle.

However, there is no evidence as to whether lambs were taken alive or as carrion, and both St John and John Colquhoun stated that sea eagles seldom took lambs but, as in Scandinavia, fed mainly on fish, birds winged by wildfowlers, rabbits, and carrion washed up along the tide-line in the winter, supplemented in the summer by young ducks and sea-birds, particularly cormorants; while the Shetland naturalists, the Saxbys, described how in 1868 a pair in Unst with newly hatched young would regularly fly eight miles to Balta Sound and 'carry off poultry from the cottage doors when the men were at the fishing, treating the women and children with the utmost contempt'.

Sea eagles continued to nest in the north-west Highlands until about 1890, and in Ireland until about 1910, four years later than the golden eagle. In Shetland there was an eyrie on Yell until 1910, when it was robbed by an English collector, reputedly a clergyman, while a female continued to visit an eyrie on Noss every year for ten years after her mate had been shot, until 1918. But the last pair of sea eagles to breed in Britain did so in Skye in 1916. It is possible, though not, one would think, probable, that at some future date sea eagles may once again have eyries in the Highlands, for after the release of four young eagles on Fair Isle in 1969 had proved unsuccessful, a similar experiment is now being tried on Rhum, where one and possibly two young birds, released in 1975, are still being sighted on or near that island, while six of ten more eaglets imported from Norway in 1976 were flying free by the spring of 1977.

There are still some 450 pairs of sea eagles in north Norway and a further 65 pairs in Iceland, whereas in Finland they have been almost exterminated, and in Sweden more than three-quarters of the 50 or so pairs are unable to breed. In both the latter countries they – and also the peregrines, whose numbers have been reduced to a handful – have been severely affected by toxic poisons, and their rate of reproduction has seriously declined over recent decades. Toxic poisons have also been responsible for a catastrophic decrease in the numbers of British raptors, just when they were beginning to recover from persecution by gamekeepers and collectors. It was in the late 1940s, shortly after such organochlorine compounds as aldrin and dieldrin had begun to come into general use, that it became apparent that there had been a sudden and significant thinning of the shells of raptors' eggs. Subsequently there was a decrease in fertility among peregrines, golden eagles and ospreys in Britain and over large areas of Europe. Then, after dieldrin and other persistent organochlorine insecticides had been introduced as seed-dressings on spring-sown wheat in the mid-fifties, the populations of several birds of prey – notably peregrines and sparrow-hawks and, locally, kestrels – decreased alarmingly. The two latter were virtually wiped out in south and east England, and by 1963 the pre-war population of 650 pairs of peregrines had been halved and only 13 per cent of these were breeding successfully following the use of dieldrin as a sheep-dip in Scotland; the breeding success of golden eagles also dropped markedly in districts where they fed largely on sheep carrion.

Organochlorines are persistently toxic, passing from one organism in a food chain to another and reaching maximum levels in animals at the top of the chain – fish-eating species or predators feeding on other birds. More recently, industrial organochlorines (PCBs) have become widely distributed among wildlife, and especially among such predators as sparrow-hawks and kestrels, while sea eagles in Sweden, feeding on both wildfowl and fish, are affected by three persistent poisons: DDT, mercury and PCBs.

In 1966 the use of dieldrin as a sheep-dip was banned, and the 250 or 300 pairs of golden eagles in the Highlands – representing a quarter of western Europe's population – are now apparently breeding normally again and are attempting to recolonise the Lowlands and also the

Lake District and Ireland. The voluntary withdrawal of dieldrin and other organochlorine insecticides as seed-dressings for spring, but not winter, wheat has also resulted in local recoveries among other birds of prey. Sparrow-hawks are, however, still very scarce in the arable counties of eastern England; and peregrines are still absent from the majority of their former breeding sites in England and Wales, and from many around the coasts of Scotland, despite a 10 per cent increase in occupied eyries since 1962. Nevertheless, so calamitous has been the effect of toxic poisons on the European and North American populations of peregrines that Britain has now become their main stronghold, with more than half the pairs in western Europe. This situation has ironically exposed our peregrines to a new hazard, inasmuch as the world-wide scarcity of falcons has led to a growing demand for them from falconers in Sweden, Germany, Spain and Britain itself. This demand has been accelerated by recent regulations restricting the import of Finnish goshawks to this country, despite the fact that every year three thousand goshawks are being shot under licence in Finland! Inevitably, Arab sheikhs are reputedly offering as much as £2,000 for young British peregrines and from £300 to £500 for week-old nestlings, with the result that dealers are systematically raiding British eyries.

24 Discovering the High Tops

It has been said that the only terrain in Britain unaffected by man's activities is the mountain top. So far as the Scottish mountains are concerned this was more or less true until the 1960s, for the native Highlanders did not visit the high tops very often, though even the 3,000-feet mosses of the Cairngorms and the Monadhliath have been sporadically grazed by cattle and sheep, while lesser hills have been consumed by fire when muir-burning has got out of control. However, the lairds and their followers must have hunted over the hills from the earliest days, and there are many old references to ptarmigants or termagents. According to the Water Poet: 'To victuall our campe, which consisteth of foureteen or fifteen hundred men and horses . . . the faulconers, fowlers and fishers supplied in superfluous aboundance . . . venison, hares, fresh salmon, partridge, morecoots, heathcocks, caperkellies, and termagents'; while in 1663 Black John Crerare leased his land and shieling in return for his services as fowler: 'To go to the hills with a sufficient lying dog and fowling-nets, and to kill wild-fowl and moor-fowls of all kinds, and to train up a fowling dog for the use of the laird.'

But there are no references to dotterel, or to the snow bunting whose wayward behaviour, irregular nesting and inaccessibility have virtually defeated the ubiquitous collector of eggs and rare birds – the only British bird to do so. Dotterel and 'snowflecks' were too insignificant to be mentioned by hunters or by the inhabitants of the summer shielings in the high places. There dotterel, buntings and ptarmigan existed in an environment that was once widespread in lowland Britain, but which is now restricted to the highest mountains. Above 3,000 feet climatic conditions and vegetation resemble those near sea level in Greenland and Spitzbergen. July temperatures above 4,000 feet on Ben MacDhui are often lower than in Baffin Land and the winds usually much stronger. The Everest climber, Frank Smythe, indeed described the winter blizzards on the Cairngorms as severer than any he had experienced in the Himalayas, while in the summer a sudden thunder-

56. A Male Ptarmigan wit the Change to Summer Plumage almost Complete

shower can precipitate a deadly onslaught of almost solid sheets of cutting hail-stones. Semi-permanent snow beds, unmelted for decades, lie here and there in the highest corries. A dwarf arctic-alpine vegetation, typically of woolly fringe-moss, clings to the windswept ridges, where these are not chaotic jumbles of boulders stained purple-black with pads of cushion-moss and pale green with whorls of map-lichen; but above 3,000 feet there are barrens of ankle-deep grit almost devoid of plant life except for wind-frayed patches of desiccated bent and sedge and small clumps of thyme-like moss-campion.

This bleak world that emerged from the snow-fields and glaciers of the Ice Age supports a relict northern flora and avifauna more characteristic of an arctic tundra than of a European alp, for the world distribution of ptarmigan, snow buntings and dotterel is mainly arctic and subarctic; though it is true that golden plover, dunlin, wheatears and meadow pipits also nest regularly, and common sandpipers, lapwings, skylarks and common and black-headed gulls irregularly on the high mosses of the Cairngorms and the Grampians. On the Drumochter hills indeed dunlin and golden plover outnumber dotterel, the highest curlew nest above the lowest dotterel and ptarmigan at 2,500 feet, and for a stretch of forty miles from Drumochter through the Cairngorms few or no dunlin nest below that level. But there is a higher density of breeding ptarmigan between 1,750 and 4,150 feet on the Cairngorms, with their abundant provender of berry-plants, heather tips and dwarf willow, than any recorded in the Arctic. If the few pairs of breeding snow buntings do not winter on their nesting hills, then the ptarmigan, with their dense plumage and thickly feathered legs and toes, are the only permanent residents of the high tops. They survive the winter storms by feeding in packs in those places that the winds have swept clear of snow, or by scratching through shallow snow with their long hard claws, which, like those of grouse, are renewed every year. At night they roost in hollows or holes in the snow, evading the wind and benefiting from the snow's insulating property, but in no danger of being buried because they burrow in exposed sites where falling snow drifts away quickly. Highland poachers knew all about the ptarmigan's roosting habits. The artist J. G. Millais was told by his mother that, as a girl, she often saw poachers catching both ptarmigan and grouse; and Millais learned the details of their technique from an old poacher living near Inverness:

> On a well-stocked grouse-moor, during a hard winter, when the snow fell early in November and covered the valleys to the proper depth for a month, he said he could easily lift a hundred brace before the close of the season . . . The poacher discovers a place on the hill where the birds are in the habit of sitting when snow has fallen. To this spot he repairs when the downfall has ceased, and before night, if possible, so that the snow may still be soft and not frozen. He is armed with nothing but a bag of oats or corn and a beer or, better

> still, champagne bottle . . . Arrived on his ground, he proceeds to make a number of indentations in the snow with his bottle, and the bottom of the cavity, just within reach of the birds, he fills up with grain, and, scattering the rest of the contents of the bag near the holes on the surface, he departs, to return next morning and collect his plunder.
>
> Unless a frost occurs the trick must necessarily be a failure, but if the cavity becomes properly hardened and the birds find the food, success is almost a certainty. A Grouse or Ptarmigan finding what to them is a great delicacy, immediately imparts the knowledge of its presence to others in the neighbourhood. They at once greedily devour all the grain that is lying around, and then turn their attention to obtaining the stores lying in the holes. Probably by straining their necks to the uttermost they may be able to reach a few grains; but this only serves to whet their appetites, and they must have more. Consequently they go on reaching till they eventually topple over into the hole, which just comfortably corresponds to their own size, and in which the more they struggle to extricate themselves the more firmly they become wedged.

The first indication that dotterel and snow buntings might nest on Highland hills came from Thomas Pennant, who was told in 1769 that both did so on the high hills above Invercauld in Aberdeenshire. Then on 6 August 1786 the redoubtable Colonel Thornton killed a dotterel and three and a half brace of ptarmigan with his tiercels on Sgoran Dubh on the western edge of the Cairngorms, and also shot another dotterel: 'Had my powder from the first been dry I could have killed seven or eight brace.' As we have seen, the Colonel conducted his shooting and hawking expeditions in the grand manner, and one of his two ascents in August of Sgoran Dubh, after what must have been a winter of exceptional snow, was no exception, as described by him in *A Sporting Tour*:

> At half-past four we were awakened and a finer morning never ushered in the day. Started at eight, found the Spey unfordable, and were obliged to ride round above four miles by the Ruthven Ferry . . . At ten o'clock we were at the foot of the mountain, the heat intense, the mercury standing at 84° Fahrenheit.
>
> A severe labour we had to ascend this mountain, as steep as the side of a house; rocky and sometimes boggy; whilst frequently large stones, on which our horses stept with apparent security, would give way, and whirl down the precipice . . . At twelve o'clock we got up to the first snow, and, before one, we thought we were near the mouth of Glen Ennoch, and then depositing our champaigne, lime, shrub, porter, etc. in one of the large snow-drifts, beneath an arch, from which ran a charming spring, we agreed to dine there. In my way up, the pointers had found some game, and I killed . . . an old

moor-cock and a ptarmigant, which I ordered to be well picked and prepared for dinner . . .

It is impossible to describe the astonishment of the whole party when they perceived themselves on the brink of that frightful precipice, which separated them from the lake below! The mountain above them, to the right, chequered with drifts of snow . . . the immense rocks to the left, separated by large fissures, the safe abode of eagles . . . appeared to them truly *MAJESTIC* . . . Let the reader figure to himself a mountain at least eighteen thousand feet above him, and a steep precipice of thirteen thousand feet below . . . then let him imagine men and horses scrambling over huge masses of stone, which, though of immense size, are frequently loose, and at every step seem as if the next would carry them off into the air beyond its edges . . .

Our dinner . . . proved an excellent one; the chief dish consisted of two brace and a half of ptarmigants and a moor-cock, a quarter of a pound of butter, some slices of Yorkshire-smoked ham, and rein-deer's tongue . . . These . . . made each of us a plate of very strong soup.

The heat on the top of the mountain was very great, at the bottom it was really an oven. I tried the temperature of water rushing under the arch of snow on which we sat . . . and it was 43½ Fahrenheit. We now drank, in a bumper of champaign (gentlemen and servants faring alike), success to the sports of the field, and, with the addition of a tumbler of sherbet and a cordial, were enabled to pack up our apparatus and proceed.

In 1821 William MacGillivray was told that dotterel were breeding above Towie in Aberdeenshire, and in the 1840s St John stated that they bred on Ben Clibreck in Sutherland. MacGillivray later described how when on Lochnagar on 15 August 1851:

I came upon a Dotterel, which flew from among the stones, pretending lameness, and hovered around, manifesting great anxiety . . . Although it was evident that the bird had a nest and young ones, as it fluttered and limped when chased, we failed in discovering its charge.

It was another 25 years before confirmation of nesting in the Highlands was finally established by a clutch of eggs taken on an Aberdeenshire hill. Yet in a couple of hours on a June afternoon in the 1950s it was possible to find eight nests containing eggs or young, spaced more or less equidistantly along a 3,000-foot spur of the Drumochter hills; for where dotterel are numerous enough to nest in colonies – as is the case in a good year on those hills – their shallow nest-cups, set among the bare rock or sunk in the fringe-moss, are very easy to find because the nests are aligned in a predictable pattern.

7. A Dotterel

Desmond Nethersole-Thompson has suggested in his monograph *The Dotterel* that in the nineteenth century there were probably as many breeding in England as there are in Scotland today, though, even so, no more than possibly fifty to a hundred pairs; and the earliest proof that they did in fact nest in Britain had been provided by a Lakeland naturalist, Dr John Heysham, in 1785: 'Some time last summer a nest of the dotterel was found on Skiddaw: the old one was killed and the eggs brought away, which were three or four in number. I saw three of them.' Fifty years later T.C. Heysham described the favourite breeding grounds of dotterel in Lakeland as invariably near or on the summits of the highest mountains, particularly those that were densely covered with the woolly fringe moss: 'A few pair usually associate together.' He added that they were becoming increasingly scarce because anglers used their feathers for flies; and by the 1920s they had ceased to nest regularly on the fells or anywhere else south of the Highlands. In the fifties and sixties, however, they began to recolonise some of the fells, at the same time that they were extending their range in their British stronghold of the Grampians.

By 1967 they were nesting on the hills of Kircudbright and Sutherland, and by 1969 in Wales. Much more remarkable is the fact that since 1961 large groups of dotterel have also begun to nest among the crops of sugar-beet, potatoes, peas, wheat and flax on land reclaimed from the Dutch pölders, where they had previously been known only as birds of passage in the spring! If there is any resemblance between this new habitat and that of the mountain mosses, it can only be that both are treeless. They have also extended their range into Austria, Italy and Poland. Collectors and anglers were probably less responsible for the temporary decline of the dotterel in Britain – where they are on the extreme western edge of their geographical distribution – than climatic vicissitudes over northern Europe. Thus during warmer phases their range contracts, but expands during colder phases.

Proof that snow buntings nested in the Highlands was also slow to materialise. On 29 August in the year of his memorable ascent of Sgoran Dubh, Thornton saw a snow bunting 'whilst stalking "ptarmigants" on the sharp angular stupendous mountains of Lochaber'; but during the next 64 years there were only two reports of potential nesting, both by MacGillivray, who was the first naturalist to work the high tops – both in the Grampians and the Outer Hebrides – and really explore them, sleeping rough while traversing from Braemar to Kingussie and from Blair Atholl to Braemar. He describes how on 4 August 1830:

> Being on the summit of Ben-na-muic-dui . . . I observed a beautiful male flitting about in the neighbourhood of a great patch of snow. Some days after, having descended from the top of Lochnager, to its corry . . I met with a flock of eight individuals flying about among the blocks of granite. They were evidently a family, the male and female being easily distinguishable from the young.

Revisiting his old haunts twenty years later, MacGillivray again encountered three buntings on Lochnager and another in the Garbh Coire Mor, where there was a permanent snow-field below Braeriach. In 1868 two pairs were seen among the rough stones on the summit of a Ross-shire hill, another pair on an unnamed hill in 1873, and several pairs and broods of young on Ben Mor Assynt in Sutherland in 1885; but it was the following year before final proof of their breeding was provided by a nest and five nestlings from Ben Mor Assynt, and 1893 before the first nest and eggs were found in the Cairngorms. They had, however, undoubtedly nested on St Kilda from time to time, and probably in Shetland too.

We now know that the few pairs of snow buntings summering in the Cairngorms invariably and significantly site their nests near the longest-lasting snow-fields, where the snow will remain until mid-July or early August, providing that these are near a steep scree of tumbled boulders, in crevices of which the nest can be built. From the snow-fields a continuous supply of melt-water trickles down the moss-padded watercourses, and this attracts a superabundant population of crane-flies, which constitute the main food of the buntings' nestlings.

As in the case of the dotterel so, too, probably more snow buntings have nested in the high corries and scree slopes of the Cairngorms since the mid-1960s than at any time since the colder decades of the late eighteenth and early nineteenth centuries. They have also nested on Ben Nevis and the hills of Ross-shire, and have prospected, if not actually nested, on the Grampians, where they have not been known to breed since the days of the Victorian naturalists. The fact that there were few records of their nesting in the Cairngorms during the milder 1920s and 1930s, but more in the slightly colder 1940s and 1950s – they have probably nested regularly since 1945 – suggests that cooler decades in Britain, associated perhaps with longer-lying summer snow-fields, have created conditions similar to those in their nearest European colonies in south-west Norway, and have attracted wintering buntings to over-summer in the Highlands and breed.

Recent decades have been notable for the southerly extension of a number of other boreal species into the Highlands, including whimbrel, Temmink's stints, wood and green sandpipers, goldeneye duck, fieldfares, redwings and bluethroats, while since 1940 occasional solitary male snowy owls have frequented the highest plateaus and ridges of the Cairngorms. They have also wintered and summered for some years on a moor in lower Speyside, where they have preyed mainly on mountain hares and grouse, and where one was criminally pole-trapped in 1967. It was in that year that these owls officially bred for the first time in Britain, when a pair reared young on the Shetland island of Fetlar, after male birds had prospected the island during the previous four years, and young were fledged in most years up to 1975. They had almost certainly previously nested in Shetland, where the first British specimen was shot in 1811, for though the majority of records during the remainder of that century were of winter visitors, others arrived in summer and might remain for several weeks, feeding on rabbits and such birds as plover and larks. Moreover, they visited various islands in Shetland – though Fetlar is not mentioned – frequently enough and in sufficient numbers for one fisherman-crofter to have killed about thirty on Unst alone before the end of the 1860s; but their visits, and also the number of owls involved, tended to be irregular, with two or three years passing without any arriving. According to nineteenth-century Shetland naturalists the owls visited Unst every winter or summer during the 1860s, and inevitably attracted the attentions of collectors paying high prices for specimens; but their activities cannot wholly account for the fact that by the end of the century the owls had become 'exceedingly rare', and that there were only half a dozen occurrences during the first fifty years of this century. Such long-term fluctuations in behaviour must be linked to variations in the climate

58. A Snowy Owl

over arctic Europe, or in the population cycles of their small mammal prey.

It is unfortunate that the current increase in the numbers of buntings and dotterel on Highland hills has coincided with a boom in grouse-shooting, stalking and skiing, which has resulted in the opening up of their sanctuary by bulldozed Land Rover roads and chair-lifts, and in the installation of skiing metropolises accommodating fifty thousand campers and caravanners annually. Never since the glaciers melted have there been so many human beings on the high tops: yet only twenty years ago a man might walk or ski all day over the Cairngorms and Grampians and not sight another of his kind. Thus far, apart from erosion in the vicinity of the skiing slopes, hiking paths and Land Rover tracks, and the dumping of actual tons of litter around the cairns on the very highest hills, the mountain birds do not appear to have been significantly disturbed; but the fact that the Cairngorm ski-lift, for example, carries large numbers of people into the very heart of the bunting and dotterel country is a matter for concern.

25 The Cry of the Gannet was All my Gladness

Man's interest in sea-birds, as distinct from that of the hunter's and fowler's, may be said to have begun in the seventh century during the nine years that St Cuthbert, Prior and sixth Bishop of Lindisfarne from 673 to 686, passed as a hermit, either alone or with two companions, on the Inner Farne island. Actually another Bishop of Lindisfarne, St Aidan, had preceded him in the Farne hermitage in 651. At that time the island appears to have been inhabited by a primitive people equipped with flint-headed arrows and harpoons, though this sea-girt rock of black whinstone and eighty-foot cliffs was no more than sixteen acres in extent at low-water and encompassed by tide-rips as treacherous as any around the coasts of Britain. With the founding of the hermitage these 'Stone Age' folk removed to the neighbouring Wedoms or Wideopens where, despite the present absence of any fresh-water wells, they are reported to have survived for a further four hundred years or so. They were remembered as demons 'clad in cowls and riding upon goats, black in complexion, short in stature, their countenance most hideous, their heads long'.

In those days, as in our own time, eider ducks nested on the Inner Farne, and these St Cuthbert fed with the greater part of the barley he raised on the thin soil, and tamed them to take pulse from his lips and to nest about his oratory of rough stone and turf roofed with sea timber and thatched with bents. The eiders still nest around and within the little chapel erected on the site of the oratory, and are as hand-tame now as they were with Reginald, monk of Durham, when in 1167 he wrote in his *Miracles of Cuthbert* that:

> In the Island of Farne there are certain creatures which, since the days of the Blessed Cuthbert, have been tame, allowing themselves to be handled not only by the inhabitants but also by visitors. They are so tame that they build their nests and hatch their eggs in the dwelling-houses. When called, they come running and place their eggs in the hands of anyone who wishes to look at them; and allow

people to cover them over and pick them up and hold them, without displaying alarm or fear. They even show their young ones to you quite happily and submit quietly to playing in your lap, and will snuggle under your clothes or in your bosom if you permit them to. Even more wonderful, if you are living on the island, they come to the table and make their nests under your bed or even under your couch; and should you take notice of them they follow you, if you wish them to. If you entice them they come flying to your hand with beating wings, croaking and whistling, and do whatever you bid them, flapping their wings together.

Two centuries later, Galfrid of Coldingham also described in his *Life of St Bartholomew* how:

From the most antient times this Island has been frequented by a certain species of bird, the name and brood of which have been miraculously preserved . . . Such is the tameness they derive from

59. Eider Ducks and Drakes

the sanctity of the place, or rather from those who by their residence in it have sanctified it, that they will allow themselves to be seen and touched by man. They love quiet, yet are not disturbed by a noise . . . some hatch their eggs close by the altar, and nobody presumes to hurt them, or even to touch their eggs without permission. Their young . . . as soon as hatched, follow their Mothers; and when they have swum over their hereditary waves they never return to the nest.

To his contemporaries and successors Cuthbert's command over the eiders seemed miraculous, though by the thirteenth or fourteenth century the monks on the Farne had become practical crofters and fishermen, selling the eiders' eggs and stuffing their long pillows with the down; and it is only during the present century that the patronymic of St Cuthbert's Duck and its abbreviated form, Culvert Duck, have begun to fall into disuse among the local fishermen. But the traditional friendship between man and duck endures, for the Seahouses fishermen still feed the wild eiders that frequent their harbour, and from your fingers they will take bread over a coble's gunnel.

In the century following Cuthbert's involvement with the eiders and also ravens on the Farne a curious poem, *The Perils of the Seafarer,* appeared in the Anglo-Saxon *Codex Exoniensis.* In detail this reads:

At times the swan's song
I made to me for pastime,
The ganet's cry
and the hu-ilpe's note;
for men's laughter,
the men singing;
for mead-drinking,
storms there the stone-cliffs beat;
there them the starling answer'd
icy of wings.
Full oft the eagle screamed,
dewy of wings.

Since the swan with a song was probably the whooper, the hu-ilpe perhaps the curlew or whimbrel, the starling possibly the tern, and the eagle the sea eagle, K. Crossley-Holland has perhaps caught the spirit of the poem more faithfully as –

The cry of the gannet was all my gladness,
The call of the curlew, not the laughter of men,
The mewing gull, not the sweetness of mead.
There, storms echoed off the rocky cliffs; the icy-feathered tern
Answered them; and often the eagle,
Dewy-winged, screeched overhead –

for the earliest English 'smiths of song', the gleemen or minstrels chanting their heroic songs to the accompaniment of the harp, while mead or ale went the rounds, responded to the wilder and stormier aspects of Nature, expressed in the mewing counterpoint of the gulls and the harsh croaking of the gannets.

But for several centuries sea-birds continued to be valued primarily as articles of food, oil and household utility, as they had been for tens of thousands of years since late Neanderthal man had left the remains of great auks in caves in Jersey and Gibraltar, and the Magdalenians a wall etching probably respresenting three of these auks in a cave near Santander in northern Spain. The bones of the latter, together with those of gannets, cormorants, shags, swans, geese, mergansers, gulls, terns, guillemots and razorbills, were also present in the shell-mounds of the Mesolithic hunters.

Not until the thirteenth century was there any mention of a colony of sea-birds other than that of the eider duck on the Farnes. Then, in 1243 and 1247 the *Petra Ganetorum* (worth 5s) is noticed on Lundy and described in 1321 as the:

> Gannets Stone, with two places near it where the Gannets settle and breed, worth in ordinary years 66s. 8d., but this year destroyed in part by the Scots. Also one tenant who should keep the said gannets during the whole season of their breeding thereon, for which service he will be quit of his rent of 2s.

The colony of gannets on Lundy was probably always a small one. In 1887 it comprised only fifteen or sixteen pairs, and their final abandonment of the island after 1909 may have been associated with the building of a lighthouse at no great distance from the Rock in the latter years of the previous century.

Although there was a reference to puffins on the Scilly Isles in 1337, it was the gannets, with their spectacular breeding colonies and fishing technique, that inspired the first lengthy description of a sea-bird since the days of the monks, when in 1518 John Major included in his *De Gestis Scotorum* an account of the Bass Rock. First alluded to in the 1447 *Codex* of the Cistercian Abbey of Cupar, the Bass Rock was subsequently to attract almost every traveller across the Border. Major described with some accuracy how:

> Round about it is seen a marvellous multitude of great ducks (which they call Sollends) that live on fish . . . These ducks . . . in the spring of every year return from the south to the rock of the Bass in flocks, and for two or three days, during which the dwellers on the rock are careful to make no disturbing noise, the birds fly round the rock. They then begin to build their nests, stay there throughout the summer, living upon fish, and the inhabitants of the rock eat the fish which are caught by them. The men climb to the nests of the

birds, and there get fish to their desire. Marvellous is the skill of this bird in the catching of fish. With lynx-like eyes he spies the fish at the bottom of the sea, precipitates himself upon it, as the hawk upon the heron, and with beak and claws drags it to the surface; and if at some distance from the rock he sees another fish better than the first that has caught his eye, he lets the first escape until he has made sure of the one last seen; and thus on the rock throughout the summer the freshest fish are always to be had . . . At the end of the autumn the birds fly round about the rock for the space of three days, and afterwards, in flocks they take flight to southern parts for the whole winter . . . These birds are very long-lived, a fact which the inhabitants have judged by marks upon some of them.

In 1526 Boece referred to the solan geese on Ailsa Craig, and in 1549 Dean Munro described how the men of Ness on Lewis sailed to Sula Sgeir, where they landed for a week or so to collect fowl and feathers; but it was not until after the middle of the seventeenth century that a naturalist explored any of Britain's great sea-bird metropolises. In 1660 John Ray, accompanied by Francis Willughby, visited the Isle of Man, where he was able to contrast the nocturnal habits of shearwaters with the diurnal ones of puffins, and stated of the former that:

They feed their young ones wondrous fat. The old ones early in the morning, at break of day, leave their nests and young and the island itself and spend the whole day in fishing in the sea . . . so that all day the island is so quiet and still from all noise as if there were not a bird about it. Whatever fish or other food they have gotten and swallowed in the day-time . . . is (as they say) changed in to a certain oily substance . . . a good part whereof in the night-time they vomit up into the mouths of their young, which being therewith nourished grow extraordinarily fat.

Then, early in June 1697, Martin Martin was, as he said, 'prompted by a generous Curiosity to undertake a Voyage through several islets to St Kilda, and that in an open Boat, to the almost manifest hazard to his life'. Although the remains of great auks have been recovered from at least ten prehistoric sites in Ireland and Scotland, including the middens of the Iron Age brochs in Caithness and Orkney, their only permanent British breeding station in historic times was probably St Kilda. It is possible that they may also have bred on the Calf of Man, and a single pair actually did so on Papa Westray in the Orkneys in 1812, while in 1769 John Wallis recorded that 'The Penguin, a curious and uncommon bird, was taken alive a few years ago in the Island of Farn.' No doubt Munro was aware that the auks bred on St Kilda, but they had probably ceased to do so regularly a decade or two

60. A Gannet Colony

before Martin's landing. However, as late as 1764 they were reported to visit the island at intervals during the 'course of years', and occasional individuals were still turning up at the island the following century when, in 1840, one was beaten to death as a witch. This incident suggests that the great auk was unknown to the St Kildans of that generation, though the oldest inhabitant was said to be able to remember three or four of them. In the meantime one had been caught off Harris in 1821, but had escaped; and in 1834 one was seen in Waterford harbour.

According to Martin's account of St Kilda:

> The Sea-Fowl are, first, *Gairfowl,* being the stateliest, as well as the largest Sort, and about the Size of a *Solan* Goose, of a black Colour, red about the Eyes, a large white Spot under each, a long broad Bill; it stands stately, its whole Body erected, its Wings short, flies not at all; lays its Egg upon the bare Rock, which, if taken away, she lays no more for that Year: she is whole footed and has the hatching Spot upon her Breast; i.e. a bare Spot upon which the Feathers have fallen off with the Heat in hatching; its Egg is twice as big as that of a *Solan* Goose, and is variously spotted, Black, Green and Dark; it comes without regard to any Wind, appears the First of *May* and goes away about the middle of June.

In the eighteenth century great auks were also breeding on islets off south-west Iceland, Greenland and Newfoundland; but their last Icelandic stations were submerged by volcanic eruption in 1830, though some fifty auks survived on Eldey. The Icelanders have also left us an excellent description of them:

> They swam with their heads much lifted up, but their necks drawn in; they never tried to flap along the water, but dived as soon as alarmed. On the rocks they sat more upright than either the guillemots or razorbills, and their station was further removed from the sea. They were easily frightened by noise, but not by what they saw . . . They have never been known to defend their eggs, but would bite fiercely if they had the chance when caught. They walk or run with little short steps, and go straight like a man.

It was typical of the age that all the Eldey survivors had been collected for museums within fourteen years of the eruption. By 1844 the world population of the great auk had been wiped out, and this is the only North Atlantic sea-bird to have become extinct, mainly because being flightless it was unable to escape from fowlers and ships' crews on the low rocks on which it laid its egg. Collectors sealed its doom. That this is the only species of sea-bird to have been lost is surprising, for all those animals, whether sea-birds or seals, that leave the sanctuary of the ocean and concentrate during the breeding season in immense aggregations on a few isolated cliffs and islands are peculiarly vulnerable not only to natural predators such as foxes and hawks, and alien ones such as rats, but also and particularly to exploitation by man, to which they are not in the main exposed at other seasons of the year.

From the eighteenth to the early nineteenth century sea-birds were slaughtered in large numbers by fowlers, by collectors for museums and fashion-houses, by pleasure-steamer parties, by sportsmen as targets and by any imbecile with a gun. At the end of the eighteenth century, for instance, the fishermen of Clovelly were reported to collect nine thousand wings of kittiwakes for the millinery trade during the first fortnight in August, when the young birds were in their beautiful black and white 'tarrock' plumage. By the middle of the nineteenth century the stock of eider duck on the Farnes had been reduced to two pairs – there are now more than a thousand pairs; and on a single June day in 1870 Henry Seebohm, an ornithologist with a world-wide reputation, took 456 eggs of various Farne species. In Orkney the red-necked phalaropes were almost shot out by collectors between 1848 and 1854, while in 1895 the St Kildans were taking the adults and eggs of the fork-tailed petrels (of which the first specimen had been obtained from St Kilda in 1818 and which bred on only three other islands in British waters – the Flannans, Sula Sgeir and North Rona) and keeping the birds in stockings until a boat chanced to call: 'When these once beautiful little birds, now starved and mauled, are offered for sale.' Collectors would, for that matter, have assuredly exterminated the population of St Kildan wrens, had their nests not been so inaccessible and difficult to find, once they had been declared a race distinct from those on the mainland. Even so, a special Act of Parliament had to be passed for their protection in 1888.

But though there was commercial egging on a large scale during the nineteenth century when, for example, 130,000 guillemot eggs were reported to have been taken in 1884 from the Bempton cliffs in Yorkshire, the more serious exploitation by fowling on a scale large enough to support the human population of an island has always been confined to a few centres such as St Kilda. There fowlers have been operating for at least a thousand years and possibly since the Iron Age, and perhaps as many as 90,000 puffins were harvested annually during the latter half of the nineteenth century, in addition to 90,000 eggs in at least one year. Various techniques were employed by the St Kilda fowlers. According to Kenneth Williamson, one entailed laying a rope, to each side of which a score or so of horse-hair nooses were attached, over a rock on which off-duty puffins were accustomed to congregate. The ends of the rope were weighted with stones. When a puffin alighted its webbed feet became entangled in a noose, and its struggles to free itself aroused the curiosity of other puffins, which also became entangled. But the majority of the puffins were caught with a rod from twelve to fifteen feet long, with a horse-hair noose at the tip. This the fowler advanced cautiously towards the nearest group of puffins until able to drop the noose over the neck of one of them. With this technique he might catch as many as two hundred puffins during the course of the day, though this harvest did not equal that of the Faeroese fowler who could sweep from three hundred to eight hundred puffins out of the air with his 'fleyging' net as they flew in a continual succession over the cliff siding.

Gannets and their eggs had also provided the St Kildans with a staple food since medieval times. Their first fowling expeditions to the gannetries were made in March in order to 'steal' the sleeping birds at night, while in the middle of May they made further expeditions for eggs. For fowling, dark nights were chosen, because it was essential to capture the sentinel over each group of sleepers, since as Martin Martin explained:

> If the centinel be awake at the approach of the creeping fowlers, and hear a noise, it cries softly, grog, grog, at which the flock move not; but if this centinel see or hear the fowler approaching, it cries quickly, bir, bir, which would seem to import danger, since immediately after, all the tribe take to the wing, leaving the fowler empty on the rock.

At daylight the fowler collected up the carcases of the gannets they had killed and tossed them down from the cliffs to the sea hundreds of feet below, where they were gathered by their fellows waiting in the boats.

According to Martin:

> The inhabitants commonly keep yearly above twenty thousand young and old in their little Stone Houses, of which there are some hundreds for preserving their Fowls, Eggs, etc. . . . They preserve their eggs commonly in their stone pyramids, scattering the burnt ashes of turf under and about them, to defend them from the air, dryness being their only preservative, and moisture their corruption; they preserve them six, seven or eight months. . .

But in this estimate Martin appears to have exaggerated, for the St Kildans probably never at any time took more than 5,000 young and adult gannets a year prior to 1829, and never more than 2,000 between 1829 and 1843. At that time the hundred or so inhabitants on Hirta were also harvesting an annual average of 12,000 fulmars. The fulmar was the multi-purpose bird, for as the Rev. Kenneth Macaulay wrote in 1758:

> Can the world exhibit a more valuable commodity? The fulmar furnishes his oil for the lamp, down for the bed, the most sallubrious food, and the most efficacious ointment for healing wounds. Deprive us of the fulmars, and St Kilda is no more.

Like other petrels, the fulmar produces stomach-oil and, 'When anyone approaches . . . it spouts out at its Bill about a Quart of pure Oil: it is good ointment against Rheumatic Pains and Aches in the Bones.' Williamson has described how, as the fowler killed each fulmar, he upended it and squeezed the body so that the oil ran from its mouth into a solan goose stomach which he carried slung around his waist.

The normal increase in the puffin population, which was of the order of millions at such metropolises as St Kilda and the Shiant Isles, was probably sufficient to offset the combined toll taken by natural predators and fowlers, but during the last hundred years there has been a catastrophic decline in their numbers along the western seaboard of Britain. In the middle of the nineteenth century and again in the early 1960s there were, for example, estimated to be three million puffins on St Kilda – though with such enormous numbers of burrow-nesting birds involved, this figure must represent a guess rather than an estimate. Even so, their present population is reckoned to be no more than a quarter of a million. Similarly on Annet in the Scillies a former population of perhaps 100,000 had been reduced to less than a hundred pairs by 1973, and that on Lundy from some 7,000 in 1939 to ninety-odd pairs, while on Ailsa Craig puffins are now probably extinct. The causes of this decline have not been precisely established, but a major factor would appear to have been the brown rats, which we know were responsible for exterminating several island colonies of the burrow-nesting Manx shearwaters during the nineteenth century. Rats, surprisingly, have never gained access to St Kilda, but they have to Lundy, the Calf of Man, Ailsa Craig and the Shiants; and though the puffins continued to breed in large numbers on these islands for many decades after the rats had invaded them, it would seem significant that all their colonies have now been reduced to skeleton strength.

In addition to the toll taken by rats the puffins have also had to contend in recent years with that enormous increase in the numbers of the larger gulls, particularly the greater black-backs which on some islands prey mainly on adult puffins, with the result that there is also a heavy mortality from starvation among the young puffins. On St Kilda the larger gulls were probably never very numerous prior to the evacuation of the human population, because they would have been competing with the ruthless St Kildans for the harvest of auks; but after the evacuation which, it will be recalled, took place in 1930, the gulls began to increase. This was partly due to the fact that they were no longer harried by the St Kildans and partly perhaps because the resident population was reinforced by immigrants, for Williamson noted that when the island was re-occupied in 1957 – by the military – some three hundred herring-gulls followed the landing-ships from their base in the Outer Hebrides and summered on St Kilda.

Finally, all sea-birds, but particularly divers such as the puffins and other auks fishing in coastal waters, have suffered a heavy mortality from oil pollution and toxic chemicals in recent years. Since the 1940s of 1950s it is possible that oil pollution has been responsible for an annual loss of between 50,000 and 250,000 sea-birds in British home waters alone. Oil from the *Torrey Canyon* accounted for at least 10,000 guillemots, in addition to an unknown number of other species, and PCBs may have been responsible for the Irish Sea 'wreck' of sea-birds in 1969, in which 12,000 or more guillemots died. However, some other unknown factor may have contributed to the general decline in the puffin population, for during the same period other sea-birds have been increasing, some spectacularly so. Kittiwakes, for example, after being reduced in numbers during the nineteenth century by the demands of the fashion trade, have increased this century, not only in Britain but all along the North Sea coast from southern Norway to France. In the 1930s indeed they began to spill over from their cliff-nesting stations in Britain and Norway and establish breeding colonies on harbour walls and buildings, and even at inland sites such as Dunston, nine miles up the Tyne.

Gannets have also increased. Since their North Atlantic population was concentrated during the breeding season at less than twenty gannetries, ten of which were in British waters, intensive fowling for food reduced this population by about two-thirds during a sixty-year period of the nineteenth century, for in contrast to the puffins' tens of millions, gannets numbered only tens of thousands. But by the early years of the present century the St Kildans had cut back considerably on their harvest of gannets and took no more after 1910, and today the gannetry on Sula Sgeir is the only one in Britain from which a (controlled) number of young gannets or gugas are still harvested annually – by the Lewis men – though exploitation on a small scale continues in the Faeroes. The result of this almost total cessation of fowling has been a steady increase in the numbers of gannets to more than 140,000 pairs, and the founding of new colonies as far south as Brittany and the Channel Isles. In 1914, for example, a single pair nested on Noss in the Shetlands, after gannets had prospected the island for two or three years. Eight years later there were still only twenty or thirty pairs, but by 1930 the colony had increased to about two hundred pairs, quadrupled in the next four years, and may now be approaching 5,000 pairs.

The invasion of a new habitat by an alien species of bird must obviously cause problems among those species already in possession. Throughout their colonisation of Noss the gannets have been peaceably but surely crowding out the guillemots and to a lesser extent the kittiwakes from their immemorial nesting ledges. Today only a few kittiwakes remain in the gannetries, thinly interspersed among the even rows and tiers of gannets, and squeezed into the cells with which the weathered sandstone is honeycombed in places. Here and there a small township of guillemots huddles up on a platform in an angle of the cliff, while others are packed tightly, a dozen together, among the gannets in those places where the latter are nesting less evenly;

there are even solitary pairs of guillemots shrinking up against the cliff wall between the drum-nests of adjacent pairs of gannets. The latter's bulky nests are spaced only twelve inches or so apart: a space, covered by the lunge of a sitting gannet at its neighbours on either side, in which a pair of guillemots may stand or even walk quietly about, but in which a resident colony is not tolerated. Photographs taken of one section of the Noss gannetry in the 1930s and subsequently illustrate how great has been the reduction in the numbers of guillemots within the gannetry, as the latter has extended along one ledge after another. Moreover, in addition to actual loss of territory, those guillemots still nesting within the gannetry lose numbers of eggs, which roll off the ledges, during the commotion caused by every alighting and departing gannet, and also a great many fledgelings, which are knocked off the ledges and seized by great black-backs and herring-gulls and to a lesser extent by great skuas. From these various causes it seems possible that, even if there were no further increases in the numbers of gannets and skuas, the vast majority of guillemots and kittiwakes must ultimately be driven from the Noss cliffs. Their expulsion might be accelerated by the increase to saturation point of the fulmars.

It will be recalled that the great skuas, or bonxies, had been protected by the eighteenth-century crofters on Foula because they kept the sea eagles and ravens away from the sheep, though at that time there were said to be only six pairs on Foula and a further three pairs on Unst. But towards the end of the next century they increased rapidly to their present strength of 2,500 pairs on Foula, and also colonised other Shetland islands, including Noss, where two pairs nested in 1910 – four years before the first pair of gannets. Thereafter, the colony on Noss grew only slowly, but by 1946, when there were 113 pairs and at least 50 non-breeding birds, a stage had been reached whereby the bonxies, after 37 years' occupation, dominated the interior of the island, having concluded the expulsion of the nesting herring gulls and lesser black-backs from the interior to the coastal surround, and their number have more than doubled during the past thirty years.

The most spectacular success story among sea-birds has, however, been that of the remarkable fulmar, the marine counterpart of the collared dove. From the time of the Vikings until 1877 the only breeding station of fulmars in Britain was St Kilda. Indeed, in the seventeenth century their only other station in the North Atlantic may have been Grimsey off the north coast of Iceland. They, too, were heavily exploited by fowlers – the St Kildans were still taking 4,000 annually in 1929; their occupation of the vulnerable nesting zone on the cliff sidings extended over a period of several months; they did not begin to breed until seven or nine years old, since their average expectation of life was at least 23 years and possibly more than 30; and they laid only one egg. Yet despite all these factors being apparently unfavourable to any abnormal increase in their population, this began to expand more than 150 years ago, when in 1820, Icelandic fulmars established a colony in the Faeroes. Nearly sixty years later St Kilda or Faeroe fulmars colonised Shetland – first, in 1878, Foula and, twenty years after that, Noss. Today, fulmars from St Kilda, or from Faeroe or Iceland, have occupied virtually all suitable sites along almost the entire coastline of the British Isles and have overflowed into Europe. More than 300,000 nesting sites have been taken over at some five hundred stations in Britain, including some inland crags and quarries five miles or more from the sea.

The reasons for this population explosion are disputed, but most ornithologists believe that it was associated with the increased availability of food in the form of offal from, in the first place, the northern whale fishery and subsequently the trawling fleets; and certainly the fulmar's highest rate of increase in the 1930s and 1940s, when the St Kilda population increased by 50 or 100 per cent, coincided with maximum trawling catches, while the significant decline in their rate of increase since the 1950s has coincided with the decline of trawling. To be able to watch from year to year birds as obvious as fulmars, whose every coming and going can be observed, actually in process of expanding their geographical range provides a rare opportunity for studying a major natural phenomenon. A pair of fulmars do not suddenly appear in a new locality one spring, appropriate a nesting site and lay an egg. No, for a number of years a few fulmars prospect a new stretch of cliffs, flying up again and again to them or sitting on the ledges for long periods, but without laying any eggs. Eventually eggs are laid and as the colony increases in size, so the time of the first visit of the year to the cliffs becomes earlier and earlier, until ultimately some birds are returning in the first week of October, though eggs will not be laid until the following mid-May or first days of June. In a large colony there is no week, and possibly no day, in the year when some fulmars are not present at the breeding cliffs, though during the winter months there may be periods of a week or ten days when none visit the smaller colonies. Such absences usually, though not necessarily, coincide with spells of stormy seas when no doubt the birds have difficulty in obtaining food. Thus, the fact that those adults that have successfully reared young do not leave the cliffs until the end of August or middle of September would seem to indicate that fulmars are unlikely to breed in consecutive years, and may perhaps do so only once in three years: yet colour-ringed birds on Eynhallow, Orkney, have been proved to lay every year.

One reason for the fulmars' success is that they are extremely adaptable in their choice of habitat. If a cliff contains ledges not occupied by other sea birds, then numbers of fulmars will take advantage of these and sit side by side as a colony, but any niche will do and a solitary pair will even rear a young bird on an inland crag a mile from its nearest neighbours. In such a situation the young fulmar when it fledges must have the ability to navigate, unaccompanied by a parent, to the nearest expanse of sea, which is not visible, may be some miles distant, and of the existence of which, indeed, it is unaware. Yet the majority of the fledgelings reared on sea cliffs cannot fly very far initially, and in many cases can only flutter down to the beach below and in due course swim out to sea. This limit to the fledgelings' flight range must therefore presumably determine the maximum distance from the sea at which fulmars can establish breeding colonies.

26 What of the Future?

It was appropriate that we should have concluded with the fulmar which, like the collared dove, is a bird with a future, even if its present expansionist phase is nearing its climax with the general decline of trawling. There are other birds with a future in Britain. Redwings have 'returned' to their Neolithic haunts in the mixed pine and birch wood fringes of the Highlands, where they have nested regularly since 1959 and some three hundred pairs now breed in more than fifty localities. Actually, Richard Jefferies chanced upon a colony of three or four redwings in a locality near the South Downs a hundred years ago. He shot one of them for identification purposes, found a nest, and watched the nestlings being reared and eventually fly.

Fieldfares, after raising three young in Orkney in 1967, are now also breeding in the Highlands, and have even done so in the Pennines. Bluethroats have attempted to breed in the birch woods of the Upper Spey, and a pair or two of shorelarks – which have greatly increased in Scandinavia during the course of this century – have summered on Highland hills. A great northern diver has reared two young ones in Wester Ross and golden-eye duck are now firmly established in east Inverness-shire, attracted by the provision of nesting-boxes.

Elsewhere, southern England is being colonised by birds from the Continent such as firecrests and short-toed treecreepers, and also serins which in the course of the past hundred years have spread northwards from the Mediterranean to northern France, Germany, Holland, Denmark and Sweden. In addition, the mild winters of the 1940s and 1950s allowed Cetti's warblers to extend their range north over France and colonise the Channel Islands, and during the past five years they have become established in Kent.

But there have been losses to set against the gains. The Kentish plover ceased to breed in Britain 25 years ago. Their south coast shingle beaches were rendered uninhabitable by seaside development and the Dungeness nuclear station. No wrynecks have nested in southern England since 1969 though, curiously, three pairs bred on Speyside that year; and the total British population of red-back shrikes – common enough in many parts of southern and central England thirty years ago – has now been reduced to about seventy pairs. We do not know why wrynecks and shrikes are deserting Britain, though it has been suggested that the shrikes' retreat may have been initiated by a scarcity of large flying insects during the period of wetter and cloudier summers. As we have seen many times in the preceding chapters, climatic vicissitudes have often been responsible for changes in the status of various forms of wildlife. Exceptionally fine weather coinciding with the spring passage of birds can result in such rarities as bee-eaters and black-winged stilts extending their migration to nest in Britain. Occasional severe winters may have contributed to the decline of the stonechat, though this might also have been brought about by the decrease in gorse-covered commons and shrubby headlands, for stonechats require look-out perches from which to espy the ground invertebrates on which they feed. Every severe winter decimates the Dartford warblers, which have never recovered from the Victorians' persecution, and their survival as a British-breeding species may now depend on the Dorset heaths being preserved from afforestation, agricultural exploitation and drilling for oil.

Sixty thousand acres of rural land are swallowed up by urban expansion every year. Agricultural land, road verges and canal towpaths are sprayed with toxic chemicals, and farms are almost fully mechanised. A million new cars a year convey ever-increasing numbers of city dwellers and tourists into the countryside, in addition to a hundred thousand naturalists of one kind or another. There are three million anglers; and lakes, broads and gravel-pits are crowded with sailing dinghies, power-boats, water-skiers and pleasure craft. The hills are invaded by tens of thousands of skiers, hikers and climbers. Yet, despite these apparently unfavourable environmental conditions, some of the rarer mammals are increasing in numbers and extending their range, rare birds are returning to localities from which they were banished in Victorian times, and new species from Europe are colonising Britain. Now that the human population increase has slowed down, can this resurgence of wildlife be maintained against so many external pressures? That there is a will that it should be has been convincingly demonstrated by a revolution in urban policy in London itself.

As recently as 1957 forty miles of the Thames from Richmond to Tilbury had become so polluted and deficient in oxygen, after having served as the metropolis' refuse dump and sewer since the time of the Industrial Revolution, that the only fish that could survive, in less polluted backwaters, were eels which could take in air at the surface. Yet on a single day in 1766 one hundred and thirty salmon were sold at Billingsgate, and the London apprentices of that century are said to have protested at their monotonous diet of salmon taken from the Thames. Early the following century four hundred fishermen were still being employed on the Deptford to Richmond reach; but although a very occasional salmon was caught in the Thames up to about 1860, all kinds of fish had virtually disappeared from the river by the 1830s. They would not reappear until 1963, after the Port of London Authority and the Greater London Council had begun a progressive clean-up of the river and its adjacent marshes. Conservation works! Today the number of species of fish frequenting the previously polluted reaches is approaching the hundred mark, and includes such fresh-water ones as the sensitive rainbow trout, together with pike, tench, carp, roach, perch, dace, bleak, rudd and chub. Moreover migratory fish, such as sea trout, can now pass through the central 'plug' of polluted water to the upper reaches, and a few salmon have got as far as the lower reaches of the Inner Thames. No less remarkable is the fact that the estuary and its reclaimed marshes now form one of the most important wetlands in Europe, attracting large numbers of winter duck and thousands of wading birds.

If such a miraculous transformation can be wrought in an environment so polluted and derelict as the Thames and its docks and marshlands, any feat of conservation is possible.

Bibliography

Atkinson, R. 1949. *Island Going.* London: Collins.

Balharry, R. 1968. 'Sweet Mart.' *Animals, 11,* 7, 292-5.

Barret-Hamilton, G.E.H. 1910-21. *A History of British Mammals.* 2 vols. London: Gurney and Jackson.

Batten, H.M. 1952. *British Wild Animals.* London: Odhams Press.

Baxter, E.V. and Rintoul, L.J. 1953. *The Birds of Scotland.* 2 vols. Edinburgh: Oliver and Boyd.

Beirne, B.P. 1947. 'The History of the British Land Mammals.' *Ann. Mag.Nat. Hist.*, ser. II, 14, 501-14.

Bell, T. 1874. *A History of British Quadrupeds.* Second edition.

Bille, R.P. 1975. *The Guinness Guide to Mountain Animals.* London: Guinness Superlatives.

Blackie, J.S. 1876. *The Language and Literature of the Highlands.* Edinburgh.

Blair, P.H. 1976. *Northumbria in the Days of Bede.* London: Victor Gollancz.

Boece, H. 1526. *Scotorum Historiae a prima gentis origina.*

Bolam, G. 1912. *The Birds of Northumberland and the Eastern Borders.* Alnwick.

—. 1913. *Wild Life in Wales.* London.

Bonner, W.M. 1976. *The Stocks of Grey Seals and Common Seals in Great Britain.* The Natural Environment Research Council Publications Series C, no. 16.

Bourlière, F. 1955. *The Natural History of Mammals.* London: Harrap.

Breuil, H., Berger-Kirchner, L. and Bandi, H.-G. 1961. *The Art of the Stone Age.* London: Methuen.

Brown, L. 1976. *British Birds of Prey.* London: Collins.

Brown, P. and Waterston, G. 1962. *The Return of the Osprey.* London: Collins.

Browne, Sir T. 1902 (ed. T.Southwell). *Notes and Letters on the Natural History of Norfolk.* London: Jarrold.

Bulleid, A. and St. George Gray, H. 1911. *The Glastonbury Lake Village.* 2 vols. The Glastonbury Antiquarian Society.

Burke, E. 1965. 'The Irish Wolfhound.' *Animals*, 5, 13, 433-5.
Burton, M. 1968. 'About Dormice.' *Animals, 11*, 6, 269-73.
—. 1973. *Animals of Europe*. London: Peter Lowe.
Caesar, J. 1966 (trans. H.J. Edwards). *De Bello Gallico.* London: Heinemann.
Cambridge History of English Literature. 1960 (eds. A.W. Ward and A.R. Waller). vol. I. Cambridge: University Press.
Cambriensis, G.de. 1863 (ed. T. Wright). *The Historical Works of Giraldus Cambriensis.*
Carr, R. 1976. *English Fox Hunting.* London: Weidenfeld and Nicolson.
Chapman, D. and N. 1975. *Fallow Deer.* Lavenham: Terence Dalton.
Clapham, R. 1922. *Foxes, Foxhounds and Fox-Hunting.* London: Heath and Cranton.
Clare, J. 1935 (ed. J.N. Tibble). *The Poems of John Clare.* 2 vols. London: J.M. Dent.
Clark, G. 1937. *Prehistoric England.* London: Batsford.
—. 1948. 'Fowling in Prehistoric Europe.' *Antiquity,* 22, 116-30.
Clarke, J.G.D. 1954. *Excavations at Star Carr.* Cambridge: University Press.
Cobbett, W. 1966. *Rural Rides.* 2 vols. London: J.M. Dent.
Collar, N. 1976. 'Bringing back the Bustard.' *Wildlife, 18,* 6, 254-7.
Colquhoun, J. 1888. *The Moor and the Loch.*
Corbet, G.B. 1966. *The Terrestrial Mammals of Western Europe.* London: G.T. Foulis.
Corbett, K.F. and Beebe, T.J.C. 1975. 'The Disappearing Natterjack.' *Oryx*, 13, 47-9.
Cornwall, I.W. 1958. *Prehistoric Animals and their Hunters.* London: Faber.
Cox, N. 1973. *The Gentleman's Recreation.* Wakefield: EP Publishing.
Cramp, S. 1965. 'The Threat to Europe's Birds of Prey.' *Animals, 6,* 2, 30-4.
—. 1971. 'Chemical Pollution and Wildlife.' *Animals, 13*, 9, 414-16.
Cranham, J. 1972. 'Farne Island Rabbits.' *Animals, 14,* 6, 244-5.
Crook, I. 1969. 'Feral Goats of North Wales.' *Animals, 12,* 1: 13-14.
Curry-Lindahl, K. 1964. *Europe. A Natural History.* London: Hamish Hamilton.
Darling, F.F. and Boyd, J.M. 1964. *The Highlands and Islands.* London: Collins.
Dent, A. 1974. *Lost Beasts of Britain.* London: Harrap.
Dixon, W.S. 1912. *Hunting in the Olden Days.* London: Constable.
Dubock, A. 1975. 'Here they come gathering nuts . . . and myths.' *Wildlife, 17,* 11, 490-5.
Dunnet, G.M. and Patterson, I.J. 1968. 'The Rook Problem in north-east Scotland' in *The Problem of Birds as Pests.* London: Academic Press.
Edlin, H.L. 1952. *The Changing Wild Life of Britain.* London: Batsford.
Ellis, E.A. 1965. *The Broads.* London: Collins.

Fiennes, R. 1976. *The Order of Wolves.* London: Hamish Hamilton.
Fisher, J. 1947. *Natural History of the Kite.* Annual Report, Royal Society for the Protection of Birds.
— 1954. *Birds as Animals.* London: Hutchinson.
—. 1966. 'The Fulmar.' *Bird Study*, 13, 5-76.
— and Lockley, R.M. 1954. *Sea-Birds.* London: Collins.
Fitter, R.S.R. 1959. *The Ark in our Midst.* London: Collins.
Frazer, J.F.D. 1965. 'The Decline of the Chalk Grassland Butterflies.' *Animals, 7,* 8, 212-15.
Gray, R. 1871. *The Birds of the West of Scotland.*
Groves, C.P. 1974. *Horses, Asses and Zebras in the Wild.* Newton Abbott: David and Charles.
Gurney, J.H. 1921. *Early Annals of Ornithology.* London: H.F. and G. Witherby.
Harrison, J. and Grant, P. 1976. *The Thames Transformed.* London: André Deutsch.
Harting, J.E., 1880. *British Animals extinct within Historic Times.*
Hawkes, J. and C. 1948. *Prehistoric Britain.* London: Chatto and Windus.
Hawksworth, D.L. (ed.). 1974. 'The Changing Flora and Fauna of Britain' in *The Systematics Association special volume,* no. 6. London: Academic Press.
Hewer, H.R. 1974. *British Seals.* London: Collins.
Hosking, R. 1976. 'In the Old Stone Barn.' *Wildlife, 18,* 3, 122-5.
—. 1977. '3 Small Mice.' *Wildlife*, 19, 1, 30-4.
Jardine, Sir W. 1838-42. *The Birds of Great Britain and Ireland.*
Jefferies, R. 1879. *Wild Life in a Southern County.*
—. 1885. *The Open Air.*
Jenkins, A. 1965. 'The Beaver.' *Animals*, 5, 19, 515-17.
—. 1965. 'The Wild Boar.' *Animals*, 5, 20, 556-8.
Kettlewell, H.B.D. 1965. 'Industrial Melanism.' *Animals, 5,* 20, 540-3.
Kyle, R. 1972. 'Goats and Sheep and the Origins of Domestication.' *Animals, 14,* 12, 534-40.
—. 1973. 'Cattle and the Course of Domestication.' *Animals*, 15, 2, 82-8.
Lack, D. 1943. *The Life of the Robin.* London: H.F. and G. Witherby.
—. 1956. *Swifts in a Tower.* London: Methuen.
Leland, J. 1964 (ed. L.T. Smith). *The Itinerary of John Leland 1536-39.* 5 vols. London: Centaur Press.
Leslie, Bishop. 1578. *De Origine Moribus et Rebus gestis Scotorum.*
Lever, C. 1977. *The Naturalized Animals of the British Isles.* London: Hutchinson.
Lovegrove, R. 1976. 'Death on the Welsh Hills.' *Wildlife, 18,* 8, 362-5.
Low, G. 1879. *A Tour through Orkney and Shetland in 1774.*
Lowe, V.-P.W. 1961. *A Discussion of the History, Present Status and Future Conservation of Red Deer in Scotland.* La Terre et La Vie. Paris: 8th Technical Meeting IUCN.

Lubbock, R. 1879 (ed. J. Southwell). *Observations on the Fauna of Norfolk.* Norwich: Jarrold.

Lynn-Allen, E. and Robertson, A.W.P. 1956. *A Partridge Year.* London: Geoffrey Bles.

MacGillivray, W. 1837-52. *A History of British Birds.*

MacKenzie, O.H. 1952. *A Hundred Years in the Highlands.* London: Bles.

MacLean, M. 1926. *The Literature of the Celts.* Edinburgh: Blackie.

MacPherson, H.A. 1892. *A Vertebrate Fauna of Lakeland.* Edinburgh: David Douglas.

—. 1897. *A History of Fowling.* Edinburgh: David Douglas.

Madden, D.H. 1897. *The Diary of Master William Silence.* London: Longmans, Green.

Marr, J.E. and Shipley, A.E. 1904. *Handbook to the Natural History of Cambridgeshire.* Cambridge: University Press.

Martin, M. 1934. 'A Late Voyage to St Kilda.' *Phil. Trans. Roy. Soc.* (1967), *19,* 6. Stirling.

—. 1970. *A Description of the Western Islands of Scotland.* Edinburgh: James Thin.

Matheson, C. 1932. *Changes in the Fauna of Wales within Historic Times.* Cardiff.

Matthews, L.H. 1952. *British Mammals.* London: Collins.

—. 1975. *Man and Wildlife.* London: Croom Helm.

Meilke, J. 1975. 'Starling Success Story.' *Wildlife, 10,* 17, 458-61.

Menzies, J.I. 1964. 'The Marsh Frogs of south-east England.' *Animals, 5,* 10, 279-80.

Millais, J.G. 1894. *Game Birds and Sporting Sketches.*

—. 1904. *The Mammals of Great Britain and Ireland.* 3 vols. London: Longmans, Green.

Moffat, C.B. 1938. 'The Mammals of Ireland.' *Proc. roy. Irish Acad.* 44 B, 61-128.

Mohr, E. 1971. *The Asiatic Wild Horse.* London: J.A. Allen.

Montagu, G. 1816. *Ornithological Dictionary.*

Moryson, F. 1617. *An Itinerary written by Fynes Moryson Gent.*

—. 1735. *The Description of Ireland.* 2 vols.

Murton. R.K. 1968. 'Darwin's Theory and the Five British Pigeons.' *Animals*, 10, 9, 400-4.

—. 1971. *Man and Birds.* London: Collins.

— and Wright, E.N. (eds.) 1968. *The Problems of Birds as Pests.* Symposia of the Institute of Biology, no. 17. London: Academic Press.

Neal, E.G. 1949. *The Badger.* London: Collins.

—. 1965. 'Britain's Carnivores.' *Animals*, 7, 5, 122-3.

Nethersole-Thompson, D. 1966. *The Snow Bunting.* Edinburgh: Oliver and Boyd.

—. 1973. *The Dotterel.* London: Collins.

— and Watson, A. 1974. *The Cairngorms.* London: Collins.

Newton, A. 1864. *Ootheca Wolleyana.*
Newton, I. 1972. *Finches.* London: Collins.
Nicholson, E.M. 1926. *Birds in England.* London: Chapman and Hall.
—. 1951. *Birds and Men.* London: Collins.
Nisbet, I.C.T. 1959. 'The Kites of Sixteenth-Century London.' *British Birds,* 52, 239-40.
Parslow, J. 1973. *Breeding Birds of Britain and Ireland.* Berkhamstead: T. and A.D. Poyser.
Partridge, L. 1975. 'Of Trees and Titmice.' *Wildlife, 17,* 12, 538-40.
Payne-Gallwey, R. 1886. *The Book of Duck Decoys.*
Pearsall, W.H. 1950. *Mountains and Moorlands.* London: Collins.
Pennant, T. 1765. *British Zoology.*
—. 1772. *A Tour in Scotland.*
—. 1883. *Tours in Wales.*
Perry, R. 1940. *Lundy: Isle of Puffins.* London: Lindsay Drummond.
—. 1946. *A Naturalist on Lindisfarne.* London: Lindsay Drummond.
—. 1948. *In the High Grampians.* London: Lindsay Drummond.
—. 1948. *Shetland Sanctuary.* London: Faber and Faber.
—. 1971. *The Watcher and the Red Deer.* Newton Abbott: David and Charles.
—. 1976. *Life in Forest and Jungle.* Newton Abbott: David and Charles.
Picozzi, N. and Hewson, R. 1970. 'Kestrels, Short-eared Owls and Field Voles in Eskdalemuir in 1970.' *Scottish Birds,* 61, 185-90.
Praeger, R.L. 1972. *Natural History of Ireland.* Wakefield: EP Publishing.
Prior, R. 1965. *Living with Deer.* London: André Deutsch.
—. 1968. *The Roe Deer of Cranborne Chase.* Oxford: University Press.
Racey, P.A. and Stebbings, R.E. 1970. 'Bats in Britain. A Status Report.' *Oryx,* 11, 5, 319-27.
Raven, C.E. 1942. *John Ray, Naturalist. His Life and Works.* Cambridge: University Press.
—. 1947. *English Naturalists from Neckham to Ray.* Cambridge: University Press.
Ray, J. 1678. *The Ornithology of Francis Willughby.*
Ritchie, J. 1920. *The Influence of Man on Animal Life in Scotland.* Cambridge: University Press.
St John, C. 1849. *A Tour in Sutherlandshire.* 2 vols. Edinburgh: David Douglas.
—. 1882. *Natural History and Sport in Moray.* Edinburgh: David Douglas.
—. 1919. *Wild Sports and Natural History of the Highlands.* London: T.N. Foulis.
St Leger-Gordon, D.F.E. 1963. *Portrait of Devon.* London: Robert Hale.
Saxby, H.L. 1874. *The Birds of Shetland.* Edinburgh: Maclachlan and Stewart.

Service. R. 1902. *A Vertebrate Zoology of Kirkcudbright.*
Sharrock, J.T.R. 1976. *The Atlas of Breeding Birds in Britain and Ireland.* Tring: British Trust for Ornithology.
Sheail, J. 1971. *Rabbits and their History.* Newton Abbott: David and Charles.
Shorten, M. 1954. *Squirrels.* London: Collins.
Silverberg, R. 1967. *The Auk, the Dodo and the Oryx.* Surrey: World's Work.
Simms, E. 1971. *Woodland Birds.* London: Collins.
—. 1975. *Birds of Town and Suburb.* London: Collins.
Southern, H.N. 1964. *The Handbook of British Mammals.* Oxford: Blackwell.
Speed, M.G. 1956. 'An Indigenous British Horse.' *Brit. Vet. J.,* 112, 483-90.
Spencer, R. 1971. 'The Blackbird.' *Animals, 13,* 17, 784-7.
Stamp, L.D. 1955. *Man and the Land.* London: Collins.
Stevenson, H. 1866. *The Birds of Norfolk.*
Storer, J. 1879. *The Wild White Cattle of Great Britain.*
Strutt, J. 1801. *Sports and Pastimes of the People of England.*
Stuart, J.S. and C.E. 1848. *Lays of the Deer Forest.* 2 vols. Edinburgh: William Blackwood.
Summers-Smith, J.D. 1963. *The House Sparrow.* London: Collins.
Tansley, E.G. 1968. *Britain's Green Mantle.* London: George Allen and Unwin.
Taylor, J. 1618. *The Pennyles Pilgrimage.*
Tegner, H. 1951. *The Roe Deer.* London: Batchworth Press.
—. 1969. *Wild Hares.* London: John Baker.
Thornton, T.L. 1896. *A Sporting Tour through the northern parts of England and great parts of the Highlands of Scotland.* London: Edward Arnold.
Turner, W. 1903 (ed. A.H. Evans). *Turner on Birds.* Cambridge: University Press.
Twigg, G. 1975. *The Brown Rat.* Newton Abbott: David and Charles.
Venables, L.S.V. and U.M. *Birds and Mammals of Shetland.* Edinburgh: Oliver and Boyd.
Vesey-Fitzgerald, B. 1946. *British Game.* London: Collins.
—. 1965. *Town Fox, Country Fox.* London: André Deutsch.
—. 1969. *The Vanishing Wild Life of Britain.* London: MacGibbon and Kee.
Waterton, C. 1871. *Essays on Natural History.*
Watt, G. 1951. *The Farne Islands.* London: Country Life.
White, G. 1905 (ed. A.W. Pollard). *The Natural History and Antiquities of Selborne.* London: Macmillan.
Whitehead, G.K. 1953. *The Ancient White Cattle of Britain.* London: Faber and Faber.
—. 1964. *The Deer of Great Britain and Ireland.* London: Routledge and Kegan Paul.

—. 1972. *The Wild Goats of Great Britain and Ireland.* Newton Abbott: David and Charles.
Williamson, K. 1948. *The Atlantic Islands.* London: Collins.
— and Boyd, J.M. 1960. *St. Kilda Summer.* London: Hutchinson.
Yalden, D.W. and Hosey, G.R. 1971. 'Feral Wallabies in the Peak District.' *J. Zool. Lond.*, 165, 513-20.
Yapp, W.B. 1962. *Birds and Woods.* Oxford: University Press.
Yarrell, W. 1843. *A History of British Birds.* 3 vols.
Zalensky, V. 1907. *Przewalski's Horse.* London: Hurst and Blackett.

Index